Lillian

BuRK

BE BRAVE
STAY WILD!

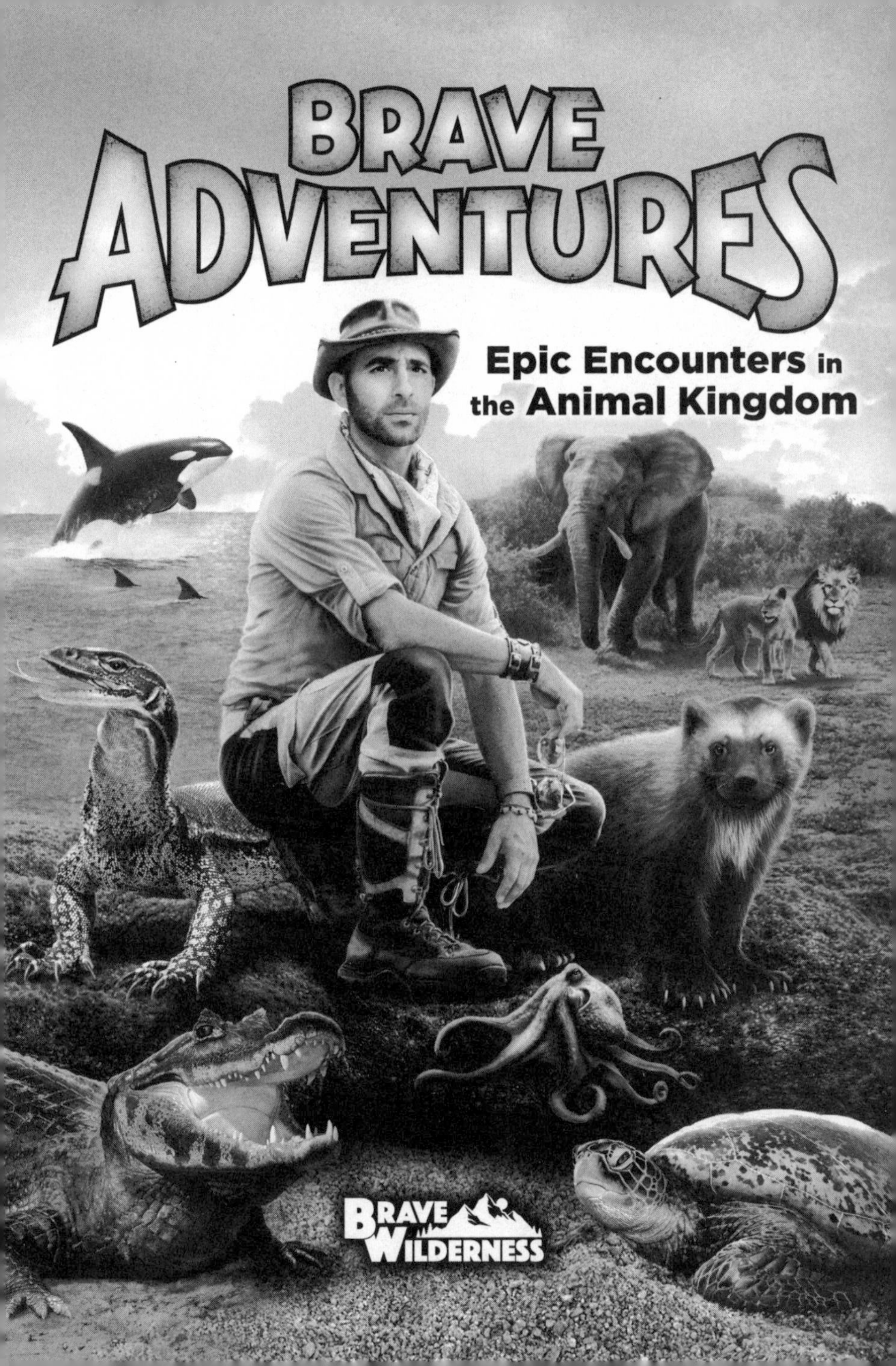
BRAVE
ADVENTURES
Epic Encounters in the Animal Kingdom
BRAVE
WILDERNESS

BRAVE ADVENTURES

Epic Encounters in the Animal Kingdom

Coyote Peterson

Little, Brown and Company

New York Boston

Hachette Book Group supports the right to free expression and the value of copyright. The purpose of copyright is to encourage writers and artists to produce the creative works that enrich our culture.

The scanning, uploading, and distribution of this book without permission is a theft of the author's intellectual property. If you would like permission to use material from the book (other than for review purposes), please contact permissions@hbgusa.com. Thank you for your support of the author's rights.

Little, Brown and Company
Hachette Book Group
1290 Avenue of the Americas, New York, NY 10104
Visit us at LBYR.com
bravewilderness.com

First Edition: September 2019

Little, Brown and Company is a division of Hachette Book Group, Inc. The Little, Brown name and logo are trademarks of Hachette Book Group, Inc.

The publisher is not responsible for websites (or their content) that are not owned by the publisher.

Library of Congress Control Number 2019937417

ISBNs: 978-0-316-45240-3 (hardcover), 978-0-316-45239-7 (ebook), 978-0-316-53735-3 (B&N special edition)

Printed in the United States of America

LSC-C

10 9 8 7 6 5 4 3 2 1

You can do anything you want....
Never give up on your dreams.

—My mom

Contents

Prologue

When I was only about eight years old, I developed a big, crazy dream for my life, and that was to host my own animal adventure show. I visualized myself introducing animal-obsessed kids like me to Earth's most fascinating, little-known creatures, such as the velvet worm—a fuzzy, fluid-filled, caterpillar-like invertebrate who roams tropical regions worldwide—or the black sea hare—a huge blob of inky black slime who resides in ocean tide pools and warm coastal waters. I was especially fascinated with reptiles, and I loved to venture into my backyard in Ohio, wading through swift-moving streams and leaping into muddy ponds to catch frogs, salamanders, and—my favorite—snapping turtles!

My backyard adventures were my research, and when I couldn't make it outside, I'd go to the library and read every book on animals I could find, or I'd watch shows like *Mutual of Omaha's Wild Kingdom* and Marty Stouffer's *Wild America*. Later on, I went to college and studied filmmaking, where I learned how to create, film, direct, and produce exciting content that would pull in viewers and keep them coming back for more.

Prologue

I worked tirelessly, never gave up, and never lost hope—even when my goals seemed difficult or hard to achieve—and in 2014, I launched the Brave Wilderness channel on YouTube. Five years later, we have over fourteen million subscribers and a show on Animal Planet, so I'm proud to say that my dreams have come true in a big way!

While I was in the midst of building Brave Wilderness, traveling all over the world and soaking up all the knowledge I could about animals and conservation, I wrote a book called *Brave Adventures* that chronicled my favorite animal encounters. From my dramatic hands-on catch of an American alligator in the Florida Everglades to my slow and painstaking capture of a tiny tropical amphibian known as the granular poison frog, these were the magical moments that built and forged my bond with the animal kingdom. Each of these wild journeys into the wilderness taught me something new about how I interact with animals, and I considered them my best adventures—the ones that started it all, taking the Coyote Pack on a thrilling, roller-coaster ride through the jungle, into the swamps, and deep into the heart of the Alaskan wilderness.

People loved reading the book, and I was overjoyed when readers wrote to me begging for more! That's where the idea for this book began. As I developed the idea for *Brave Adventures: Epic Encounters in the Animal Kingdom*, I hoped to take my fans on another set of amazing adventures, but this time, I wanted to offer something else—something bigger, more personal, and longer lasting. Over the years, I've learned so much about

Prologue

myself, my crew, the animals I've featured, and what's motivated my dedicated ambition, and I realized I could impart those life lessons to all of you. I've never set out on a big journey with blinders on. I've always had a goal, a plan, and a work ethic, and by putting all those things into practice, I've made my dreams come true. You can do the same. This book won't just take you on another fantastic and colorful voyage to the animal world; it will also advise you on some of the many ways to achieve your biggest, craziest, most-wished-for goals. I hope you read it and come away with a little inspiration, an enriched imagination, and a renewed love for the animal kingdom!

It may take your whole life for you to realize your dreams, but they *can* come true, whatever they are. So grab your passport, put on some bug spray, make sure your shoelaces are tied, and turn the page to join me on my most meaningful and thrilling adventures in the amazing, action-packed place we call nature!

Chapter One
Journey to Snake Island!

Chapter 1 / Journey to Snake Island!

In order to make your biggest, grandest, most epic dreams come true, you need to start somewhere—and that place is right at the beginning. Before Jacques Cousteau dove to extraordinary depths in the world's great oceans, explored intricate shipwrecks and coral reefs, or taught the world about marvelous marine creatures like the sperm whale and giant squid, he had to first learn how to navigate the seas. Before the late, great Steve Irwin opened his own zoo or wrestled the planet's fiercest and most frightening crocodiles using only his cunning and brute strength, he had to learn how to handle and care for the smallest reptiles. And before Bear Grylls traversed the vast, icy terrain of the Himalayas to conquer the world's highest peak, Mount Everest, he had to first learn how to hike mountain trails.

All three of these famous, fearless explorers inspire me on my adventures, and I'm proud to include them among my heroes. But ever since I was eight—when I first dug my boots into the swampy Ohio mud and launched myself onto a snapping turtle's spiked shell—I've never held the illusion that I could reach their level of expertise overnight. I always knew that my dreams of encountering the Earth's most unique and exotic creatures, building a successful animal adventure channel, and teaching the world about conservation would take every bit of energy I had. Even with a great team, the right amount of luck, and lots of hard work and creativity, I knew I had to build up my most breathtaking visions from scratch.

Every big journey starts with a first step, but the great thing

I've learned is that you can find inspiration *anywhere*. Your idols don't have to be famous, and the peaks you wish to summit don't have to be far away. Your dreams can start in the places you know the best, even right in your own backyard. For me and the Brave Wilderness team, I'm happy to say it all began in a familiar yet magical place. A place that's always been near and dear to my heart: Ohio's North Bass Island, or—as I like to call it—Snake Island!

North Bass is the northernmost US island in the Bass Island archipelago, which is a collection of small islands located in Lake Erie, near Sandusky, Ohio. Now, I know what you're thinking: *There are islands in Ohio?!* There sure are! Lake Erie is home to more than thirty islands! Out of those, eighteen reside in the US, and fourteen are considered provinces of Ohio. This amazing chain of islands formed during the Pleistocene glaciation, when gigantic ice sheets gouged deep impressions into the continental bedrock that filled with freshwater as the ice retreated. The islands begin about three miles north of the Ohio mainland and span across the Ontario border into Canadian waters. On the American side, there are a handful of small, scarcely inhabited islands with names like Sugar, Rattlesnake, and Green, but the islands I'll be talking about are the three larger Bass Islands.

At fewer than two thousand acres, the most populated of the larger islands is South Bass. Its main town of Put-in-Bay swells in the summer with plenty of fun-loving tourists who arrive there by ferry. Just north of it is Middle Bass, a lush, easygoing summer spot that was once so packed with wildflowers that it was nicknamed *Île des Fleures*, or "Island of Flowers," by the explorers who discovered it in 1679. A mile and a half north of Middle Bass is the much smaller North Bass, which is mostly protected wilderness, and where only a handful of people live year-round. These islands are a modern-day Brigadoon—an enchanting, unspoiled world like no other—and when you step onto them, you feel as if you've traveled back in time. When visiting, I don't even think to check my phone or watch TV, as the outside world and its fast-paced chaos seem to simply fade away. I don't fret over urgent tasks or chores, because here, everything can wait until tomorrow. Instead, when the hot summer sun rises high in the sky and stays out long into the evening, you will find the residents of Bass Island strolling to the park, or out on their front porches, lemonade in hand, painting or writing, listening to classic tunes from the '50s to the '80s.

I started going to the Bass Islands when I was a teenager, and it was where I honed my love for adventure. The shores, wetlands, and woodlands are teeming with animals like Blanding's turtles, fox snakes, chestnut-sided warblers, red-tailed hawks, and a menagerie of other creatures. Brave red foxes, white-tailed deer, and even coyotes cross the ice from the mainland to the islands when Lake Erie freezes over in the winter. Dozens of other mammals like cottontail rabbits and raccoons roam free across this contained—yet vast—expanse of pristine land. For me, the big adventure was kayaking from Middle Bass to North Bass—a forty-five-minute mile-and-a-half trek across water that can either be flat and glassy or peaked and choppy, depending on the Lake Erie winds. With

the sunrise spilling in through the cloudless sky, cascading a golden light across the lake, I used to love rowing to North Bass in the early morning and landing on the shore alone. With no people in sight, it was just Coyote Peterson and the silent natural landscape. To this day, it is still one of my favorite summertime excursions. Making that row across the lake washes me with energy and fires up my senses, inspiring a rush of adventure and creativity from within me. It was on North Bass that I started taking photographs of wildlife, envisioning my life as an animal explorer.

Anything and everything seems possible on tiny, remote North Bass Island, and that's why I had no doubt it was where Chance, Mark, and I would film our first episode for the Brave Wilderness channel in the summer of 2014. The question was, which animal would we spotlight? Would it be the Blanding's turtle, a rare species with a spotted shell who eats leeches and snails and spends winters under the ice? Or maybe we'd pick the giant American bullfrog, a common amphibian that is quite plentiful in the small swamps found in the interior of the islands. When it came time to begin production, the choice became clear. The Bass Islands are famous for housing a reptile that is entirely endemic to this area—a magnificent yet misunderstood species who balances out the ecosystem and has fascinated me since I first learned of its existence: the Lake Erie water snake. This aquatic snake species has not only been the nucleus of my island adventures, but it was also the reptile whose episode helped to launch the Brave Wilderness channel!

Chapter 1 / Journey to Snake Island!

Closely related to the northern water snake, the Lake Erie water snake is nonvenomous and ranges from about a foot and a half to three and a half feet in length. As juveniles, the snakes have starkly contrasting bands of black, brown, and yellow, which fade over two or three years as they mature. Though highly variable, the adults appear slate gray with pale-yellow bellies, their faint banding only slightly visible with a closer look. They hibernate underground in the winter, but during the warm summer months, they come out early as the sun rises and bask on tree branches, or on the massive limestone breaker walls that line an old dock on the south side of the island. Like all reptiles, these snakes are ectothermic, so they rely on the sun to heat up their bodies, storing thermal energy. Once they've warmed up, they become active, and at midday, they dive into the tepid lake to hunt for food.

Although once abundant across the island shores—and sometimes people's backyards and boat docks—the Lake Erie water snake was listed as a federally endangered species in August of 1999. These snakes are nonvenomous but have adapted the unique ability to mimic the unmistakable triangular shaped heads of dangerous pit vipers. When threatened by predators, they flatten out their bodies and puff up their heads to resemble the venom glands on water moccasins, copperheads, and rattlesnakes. As new, uninformed residents flooded the islands in the early 1900s, they encountered these gray-and-brown banded, three-foot long slithering reptiles everywhere. The snakes' defensive display and tendency to strike when handled instilled fear into the minds of incoming humans, and in an effort to eliminate the potential hazard, the snakes were destroyed by the thousands.

Fortunately, the tides started to turn for the Lake Erie water snake in the last few decades as inhabitants on the Bass Islands realized they were harmless, and, as early as 1977, put measures in place to protect them. In August 2011, they were removed from the US Fish and Wildlife Service's list of threatened species, and since then, their population has continued to flourish. While certainly beneficial for the snakes, these conservation projects have proven to be even more beneficial for the well-being of the larger Lake Erie ecosystem. That's because 90 percent of the water snake's diet is made up of round gobies, an invasive fish species that's damaged large populations of native fish like the Lake Erie perch and smallmouth bass. A dusky, slimy, bottom-dwelling fish with paddle-like fins that protrude out from the sides of its body like two creepy, shrunken hands, the round goby was accidentally introduced to the lake by cargo ships in the 1990s. Underwater chaos has been brewing ever since, and the only thing that's kept them in check is their number one nemesis: the Lake Erie water snakes! Acting as an environmental cleanup crew, their constant predation has prevented the goby's population from exploding to unmanageable proportions.

Chapter 1 / Journey to Snake Island!

Mark, Chance, and I knew that North Bass would be teeming with water snakes on the hunt for gobies that late-summer morning, so we loaded up our kayaks with camera equipment and started paddling. A band of brothers embarking upon our first great adventure, we cut across the uneven water, bypassing the smaller Sugar Island and approaching North Bass's shores just as the sun reached over the tops of the trees. Scanning a number of inlets for the calmest water we could find, we steered our vessels into the waters of a beautiful cove. The beach looked as if it were covered in white sand, but was actually covered with zebra mussel shells, which are so sharp that stepping on them barefoot is like walking across a field of broken glass. We stepped out of our kayaks into the clear, warm water, pulled them onto the shore, and then unpacked our gear.

"We made it!" I yelled to Mark and Chance, so thrilled to start my search that I could hardly stand it. We prepared the cameras, gathered the GoPros, and waded up the coastline through the gentle tide. This was our moment. It was Lake Erie water snake or bust. Coyote Peterson and the Brave Wilderness crew were about to transform our dreams of making animal adventure videos into a reality!

We walked gently along the shore and immediately saw a few smaller snakes basking on the rocks and limestone outcroppings. We could have easily grabbed one, but our goal was to catch a big snake, something that would be impressive on camera and that would reflect these reptiles' high levels of intensity. The best time to do that was midday, when snakes

14

were returning from their hunt for round gobies, so we had a few hours to walk around the island and film environmental B-roll shots.

This is one of the most inspiring places in the world, I thought, noticing the sounds of nature coming from every direction. Waves gently lapped on the shore line, and gulls circled and called overhead. A leopard frog croaked from out of sight, hunkered down and hiding in the marshy wetlands of the nearby woods. I smiled with pure happiness; North Bass was my home away from home, and it was about to provide us with the adventure of a lifetime.

"Let's go back toward the water to look for snakes," I said to Mark and Chance as the sun passed its highest point in the wispy sky. "They should be much more active now that the temperatures are beginning to heat up."

Back at the mussel-covered cove, I waded shin-deep into the water, holding a long stick with my camera affixed to the end of it, while Mark and Chance stayed on the shore and filmed me. I had barely gotten my feet wet, when I noticed something out of the corner of my eye, and then I heard Mark yell.

"Oh look!" he said. "It's behind you!"

Sure enough, a baby Lake Erie water snake had noticed us. Taken by surprise, it darted out from the sunny beach into the water. Anxious to escape, it swam out toward the open lake, crossing just under my legs. Without hesitation, I thrust my hands down into the water and gently scooped up the tiny reptile.

Chapter 1 / Journey to Snake Island!

Unlike many other snake species, Lake Erie water snakes are ovoviviparous, which means female snakes retain their eggs inside their bodies, where they hatch and are eventually born as live young. From mid-August until September, females hatch an average of twenty-three baby snakes each. Spotting these little guys is relatively easy, due to their banding, still striking and opaque, as they have yet to develop the dull camouflage they'll display as adults. They're absolutely adorable, and as I brought it up toward the cameras, I anticipated how squirmy and slippery it might feel in my palm.

"*WOOOW!*" I said as I cupped it in my hands. "That…is a baby Lake Erie water snake!"

This newborn was about as calm as could be. I delivered a few key facts and set it back into the water. Under the right conditions, an adult water snake can live to be about twelve years old, so I wished the best for this little one, knowing that a long life meant plenty of successfully gobbled-up round gobies! Then I turned back to the task at hand…searching for a much larger specimen.

Big snakes live to hunt. Each and every morning, these reptiles wake up, bask in the sun, and lazily bide their time until conditions are right for a hunt. Then they dive beneath the surface, where they will explore along the lake's basin and wait for unsuspecting gobies. Gobies are bottom-feeders, and their weird buggy eyes make them look more like amphibians than fish. When the gobies come along, their fins scraping on the lake floor as if they're crawling, the snakes make their stealthy approach. Then—*boom*—they strike! With tiny, needlelike teeth, they grip the struggling fish and eventually immobilize it. It takes a long time for a snake to finish its meal, and if they're submerged beneath the lake's surface, there's a risk of swallowing water and drowning. So with the goby clutched tightly between their jaws, they swim for shore, their heads just above the water, like little periscopes. While making the trek to solid ground, they keep one eye to the sky, looking out for predators like hawks or eagles, who would love nothing more than an easy meal! After reaching land, they manipulate their jaws to open their mouths as wide as possible, and hastily work the slimy fish down their throats as fast as they can. To a human, a goby would

probably taste horrific, but the snakes sure seem to love them! This is a day in the life of these amazing snakes from spring to late fall. In the winter, when the lake freezes over, they hunker down in underground burrows for a long, well-deserved rest.

The sun was dropping lower in the sky, and I knew the snakes would be returning to shore for the day. With our window of opportunity closing, Chance, Mark, and I needed to devise a plan that would ensure an encounter, but wouldn't separate a snake from its well-earned meal.

"Let's stick to the rocky shoreline. We should find a snake either coming in without a goby or going back out to hunt for more," I said off-camera.

My team agreed that this seemed like the best plan to find our target while causing the least disturbance to the snake. The water snake is at its most vulnerable when it's close to shore, so that's when it would be easiest to capture. Even though Lake Erie is usually calm, small waves crash against land just like in the ocean, creating swirling currents that are a lot to handle for a creature who barely weighs a pound. As the snake struggles to hold its head above the turbulent water, it loses visibility. While fighting to regain focus, it's blind to potential predators—or perhaps an adventurer named Coyote Peterson, who wants nothing more than to get this fascinating animal up close for the cameras.

Wading just a few feet into the crystal-clear water, I surveyed the gleaming surface, looking for the telltale signs of a snake desperately swimming for shore, or venturing out for their next yummy goby snack. Would I see a tiny head pop up scouting for predators? Or would I spot a slithering body just below the surface? These snakes were usually *everywhere* right as the sun started its decent in the late afternoon, so I knew it was only a matter of time until one crossed my field of vision.

I looked over at Mark and Chance, who were standing at the shore, their cameras positioned for action. I had a feeling something was about to happen, so I told them, "Be ready to roll cameras—it's go time!"

Boy, was I right! Before I even finished my sentence, I noticed a water snake about twenty feet from me slither off a rock into the water. In my right hand, I was holding a long stick with a camera attached to it. I took off at a sprint, water splashing up around me as I hurtled toward the snake. Unaware, it ducked under the surface to avoid the ebbing currents and slowly swam in my direction. As soon as it breached the surface, its beady eyes spotted me. It doubled back, making a lightning-fast turn and darted for the open water. But I was just as quick! Without hesitation, I dropped my stick and waterproof camera, and crash-landed in the shallow water, cutting in front of the fleeing reptile. The toughest thing about catching water snakes is that you have to synchronize your grab with their movement and aim just ahead of them so that as you make your move, you land your grip right in the center of the snake's body. Hopefully predicting the snake's path, I thrust my hand into the lake with a splash, and *boom*…I clasped my fingers around the reptile I'd been hoping to catch all day!

Chapter 1 / Journey to Snake Island!

I make it sound easy, but I've been catching snakes for decades, and I knew the positioning of my hand was important. If I grabbed the snake too far back, toward the part where its body narrowed into its tail, I might injure it. I also understood that, while Lake Erie water snake aren't venomous, they can be aggressive, so if I didn't grab it far enough from its head, it might thrash backward, strike, and try to bite me. Upon being caught, this snake was immediately thinking, *Something's caught me, and maybe if I chomp down on it and draw some blood, I'll startle it and make my escape.*

I drew the snake toward the surface of the water and breathed a sigh of relief. Like an arrow hitting a bull's-eye, I'd made an ideal catch. I'd secured the snake in my hand right at the thickest part of its body. I wasn't going to damage its tail, and thus far I hadn't been bitten.

But here's a secret: In order to create a little drama in this pioneering Brave Wilderness episode, Mark, Chance, and I were actually *hoping* I'd take a bite. One of our main intentions for our videos was to show you that many of nature's most misunderstood species—like the Lake Erie water snake, who'd been nearly wiped out by ignorant, terrified humans—tend to react defensively, even though they are nonvenomous and a bite is little more than a shot at the doctor's office. So, when I went straight into presentation mode, turning my attention away from the snake and toward the camera, I didn't care that it reared back, opened its jaws, and...

"*Ow!*" I yelled as the snake chomped down on the middle

finger of my left hand. "He just took the tip of my finger and sliced it open!"

Lake Erie water snakes don't have fangs as pit vipers do. Instead, they have small, fixed teeth with sharp points like the tip of a pin. While the bite I sustained hurt even less than a bee sting, you would not believe how much blood there was! The snake's saliva contains proteins with anticoagulant properties that prevent your platelets from clotting, allowing blood to flow from a teeny-tiny cut faster and much longer than it normally would.

Sure, it all seemed like an intense, high-action, dangerous situation, but when I looked down at my hand, all I could see were a few tiny pinprick-like puncture wounds that I knew I would clean up with a little soapy water and a Band-Aid.

Now, this was an impressive snake I held in my hands. Not only was it larger than most other water snakes I'd seen on the island—probably a good three and a half feet in length—it was also more aggressive and defensive than I'd expected. The snake didn't just sit there, thinking, *Oh well, I got caught.* This whopper of a reptile puffed up its body and flattened its head defensively, then continued to writhe around, trying to get away. A true demonstration of just how ferocious these snakes can be if humans try to interact with them.

By remaining gentle and calm, and dipping it in the water— which helps relax water snakes—I finally managed to get the creature under control and safely to shore. With both hands now shuffling its body, I knelt down to the crushed shells of the beach as an air of harmony settled over the scene and the snake examined its situation. I experience this post-catch calm demeanor quite often with reptiles, and I believe that they come to realize two things: that I respect them, and that I am not attempting to cause them harm. I kept my hands held open out in front of me to allow the snake to move freely. "The reason I wanted to catch this snake today," I said, "is so you could get the chance to see a species that was almost wiped off the face of the planet." The snake gently glided through my fingers as I admired it.

"These guys camouflage so incredibly well," I continued, setting the snake onto a wet boulder nestled on the shore. "You see that? He blends in almost perfectly with the coloration in these different shades of rock." The cool water of the lake lapped gently on the snake, and its gray, brown, and pale banding gleamed in the sunlight, just like the reflection off of the rock where it sat. Incredibly, I wasn't exerting any force on the snake at all. It was perfectly calm, flicking out its tongue as it calmly surveyed the scene around it.

That's one of the amazing things about these animals; they're perfectly attuned to their environment. This was a monumental step forward for me and the Brave Wilderness crew, and for a few short moments, I paused to let it all sink in. *This is only the beginning.* My first official animal presentation had almost wrapped, and I could not have hoped for a more cooperative and dynamic subject than this amazing Lake Erie water snake.

With the sun getting low in the sky, it was time to release the reptile back into the wild. I knelt down and opened my hands, marveling at this magnificent reptile as it slowly dipped its head under the water, slinking side to side until it was out of sight. "It's time to head back to the mainland!" I said before I gave my classic sign-off: "Be Brave…Stay Wild—we'll see ya on the next adventure."

The Lake Erie water snake is a true hero of the Bass Islands, coming back from the brink of destruction to battle the round goby, just when the islands needed it the most. This snake is an icon for the ideal interplay between man and nature, and I'd found it right in a place I knew better than almost anywhere else.

That familiarity, Coyote Pack, could be one of the secret ingredients to making your dreams come true. Find something you love, or something that inspires you—and then soak it up.

Learn from it. Let it take you to the next level. The Bass Islands have always inspired me, but on this summer day I left North Bass with the seed of a dream finally germinating in my heart. The dream of an animal adventure series that the world could enjoy. I'll never forget how my incredible journey began with the one and only Lake Erie water snake!

Chapter Two
The Ultimate
Tide Pool Adventure!

Chapter 2 / The Ultimate Tide Pool Adventure!

Before the Brave Wilderness team heads out on location to film an animal encounter, we always do our homework. We tirelessly research the type of animals we hope to find, scout out the location, talk to any experts in the area, and make sure we've got all the equipment and permits we might need in order to bring dramatic and educational animal segments to life. We also never travel somewhere unless we're positive we'll catch *something* of interest to the Coyote Pack. Can you imagine spending weeks carefully preparing, getting anxious and excited about coming face-to-face with a friendly manatee, angry bullet ant, or bizarre sea hare, only to set off on an adventure and come up dry? That would be awful—for us *and* for all of you!

I know that chasing my dreams requires meticulous preparation and lots of forethought. But if there's anything I've learned, it's that all the planning in the world won't stop the unexpected from happening. The skies might open, sending a torrential gush of ice-cold rain onto our heads; the creature we're hoping to encounter might be more elusive than we'd imagined; or I might sustain a painful bite or sting *that wasn't planned*. Thankfully, we have had amazing luck filming on location, and more often than not, we've run into incredible scenarios that I could have only hoped for in my wildest dreams!

In March 2018, Mark, Mario, and I traveled to the heart of the South African savanna to film a series of episodes on the Kariega Game Reserve. This immense, breathtaking plot of private land is home to a pride of lions, herds of elephants, and many more iconic native species. Our trip to Africa's southernmost country had been planned to a T, and upon reaching its conclusion, we'd successfully filmed all the animals on our wish list: a highly dramatic encounter with two young elephants who'd battled each other tusk-to-tusk? Check! Getting up close and personal with a tranquilized male lion and studying his powerful teeth and razor-sharp claws? Consider it done! We'd gotten all the footage we needed for two unforgettable episodes, but when our location expert—a real go-getter kind of dude named LB Williams, who runs a wildlife group called the Reserve Protection Agency—told us that he might have another adventure in store, we were all keen to accept!

"You guys want to head to the coast to see the beach?" LB asked. "If we hike a ways down from the spot I have in mind, there's a craggy, coastal area scattered with beautiful, crystal-clear tide pools."

"Absolutely!" I answered, practically jumping out of my skin. We've filmed a few episodes, known to the Coyote Pack as *Beyond the Tide*, in locations such as Costa Rica, Hawaii, Maine, and Washington, but this would be our first intercontinental tide-pool exploration. It was the chance of a lifetime!

Tide pool episodes are honest-to-goodness treasure hunts, and you never know what spectacular species you'll stumble across hiding in the rocky crevices or in the shallow, isolated pockets of water, waiting for the tide to return. You might

encounter spiky black urchins,
multicolored tropical fish,
scuttling hard-shelled crabs,
or, maybe, if you are really,
really lucky, a baby shark!

I knew that exploring
tide pools was risky, though.
Some of the animals who wash up
are incredibly dangerous, like the highly venomous blue-
ringed octopus. This species of octopus, native to the Pacific
and Indian Oceans, has a bite that contains enough toxicity
to take the lives of twenty-six grown adults. Then there's the
cone snail, a predatory mollusk whose single harpoon, shaped
like a hypodermic needle, can kill you with one vicious prick.
Preparation is everything, and you must always be ready to
encounter biological land mines like these. I will often carry a
field guide in my adventure pack, which allows me to properly
identify each and every animal we come across. Then, before
trying to catch or handle it, I double-check with Mario, whose
expertise as a wildlife biologist has never let me down. I always
expect the unexpected—the last thing I ever want to do is be
careless.

Mark, Mario, LB, and I piled into our location SUV and
bumped down dusty roads. We drove from Kariega to an area
called Kenton-on-Sea, a tiny beach community about five
hundred and fifty miles due east of Cape Town. Located on
South Africa's Sunshine Coast at the intersection of the Indian

and Atlantic Oceans, it boasts a white-sand public beach, where a handful of sunbathers lazily reclined in beach chairs. We eagerly leaped from the truck and took in our surroundings. The beautiful blue water lapped against the shoreline, and it was clear that the tide was on its way out, which meant our timing was perfect for an adventure. LB said it was going to be about a thirty-minute walk down the coast to the spot where he promised we'd come across a plethora of tide pools.

"I hope you're ready," he said with a smile. "This place is unlike anything you've ever seen."

Envision the unexpected, I told myself. *It's going to be a wild day!*

———————

I'd completely underestimated the majesty of the South African coastline. As we moved away from the populated pristine beaches toward a harsh, rugged location, the ocean became more unforgiving, crashing against rocks that tilted up toward the sky and sending a spray of foam in every direction. These towering structures looked as if they'd been dropped onto the sand by giants, and they were covered with a layer of slippery algae. I had to precisely calculate every step so that I didn't accidentally plunge into the sea or fall headfirst onto the jagged ground under me. It felt as if we had journeyed to a location one might imagine in Lord of the Rings. It was a dramatic, treacherous, Mordor-esque landscape, the kind of place that one might only conjure in the depths of imagination. On top of porous, flat, exposed rock, out near the disappearing tide, we immediately spotted a few tide pools. When we peered into them, however, all we could see was rockweed and green tubular plants called dead man's fingers.

"Hey, LB," I called out. "I thought you promised a plethora of aquatic life!"

LB laughed and shook his head with a smile. He could tell I was just teasing him. With tide pools, it's all about being patient. At this time of day, the tide was only just beginning to recede, and we still had hours of searching ahead of us. The magic of tide pools comes when the tide has reached its lowest point, allowing you to access the basins closest to the water's edge. It's usually here where you may find a beautiful world of stranded starfish—and potentially some of the more elusive tide-pool creatures.

The four of us continued down the coast, carefully navigating the terrain and constantly eyeing the ground to make sure we didn't miss a hiding creature. We rounded a corner and encountered a monolith that had been hollowed out by the briny sea. As I peered into the cavern, I saw what looked like a bright metropolis of tide pools and cliffs just beyond the end of the tunnel. Bent low, we walked through, then exited toward a series of oddly tilted low cliffs pockmarked by the savage sea. There, spread out before us was a collection of pools that stretched farther than the eye could see. This was it! Pure gold: the mother lode of tide pools, with potentially hundreds of aquatic species tucked within the millions of nooks and crannies.

"Okay, be ready to roll cameras, guys!" I yelled to Mark and Mario. "We are definitely in the right spot for creatures."

We were prepared. I had my net, my field guide, and attached to a long extendable pole, called an AquaPod, was my GoPro camera. This allowed us to film underwater with minimal disturbance to any marine life. I walked carefully up to a pocket of water and noticed everything within it: bright, colorful sea urchins lining the sides of the rocks, a few several-inch-long tan-and-black klipfish perched on the edges of tiny cliffs, and a brownish crab sitting at the bottom, completely still. It was like my own little fish tank, prepared by nature just for me. I quickly plunged my net into the water, blindly reaching toward the bottom. I could barely see, but I continued to scoop.

Bingo! On my first try, I netted the crab!

This was a good-size crustacean, gleaming like a penny with stripes down each of its legs. I carefully peeled the net away from its body, but unable to immediately identify the species, I turned to Mario, who had our marine life field guide. I had taken my eyes off the crab for all of three seconds when, in a flash, it scuttled from the net and plopped into the water. *"OH NO!"* I hollered. Without thinking, I dropped the field guide, grabbed the net, and plunged it back into the tide pool. With a sweeping scoop under the ridge of a wide rock, I dragged the lip of the net lightly across the sand and up. As I lifted the net above the surface…*SCORE!* Two klipfish in one scoop! With my catch in hand, I moved over to more solid ground and…wait a minute…

"There's the crab!" I shouted, as I plunged my net—which still held the klipfish—back into water to recover it. I brought the net back up—almost setting it down again—and marveled at my catch.

This was turning out to be one epic encounter!

Let's pause for a second, Coyote Pack. Have you ever had one of those movie-like moments when you experience something so surreal that the film of your life slows down? When you can hear your pulse, and your stomach turns over? While I was holding the klipfish in the palm of my hand, with their long dorsal ridges and guppy-like tails, something slinking in the tidepool caught my eye. I focused my gaze on the rocks and saw what appeared to be tentacles waving ever so slightly through the water.

"Oh my gosh," I said incredulously. "There's an octopus."

The octopus is considered the holy grail of tide pool creatures. You always hope you'll find one, but they are so elusive that you're truly lucky if you actually see one in the wild! It's not that octopuses don't exist near the shore; quite the opposite, they're usually prevalent. But when the tide goes out, these highly intelligent creatures blend perfectly into their

surroundings, allowing them to stay completely out of sight…
most of the time.

Like so many of the fascinating creatures I've encountered,
the octopus has adapted so perfectly to its environment that
it can often avoid detection and escape its predators. Except
for their narrow, beaked jaws, their entire body is malleable,
allowing them to wiggle and squeeze into any crack or crevice
wider than their beak. They're also capable of camouflage,
and can morph themselves to resemble rocks, coral, and other
marine features. When they decide to flee, they whiz away in
the blink of an eye, jettisoning water through their heads like
powerful pumps. If you *do* avoid the distracting spray of black
ink they spew and catch them, they're as wet and slimy as a huge
booger. Make no mistake, they'll twist and slide themselves

right out of your hands, into the water, and quickly retreat into a small hole too tight for anything but an octopus.

Suffice it to say, catching this one was going to be incredibly difficult. Was I ready? Absolutely! But first I had to prepare, and that meant turning to my field guide.

While all octopuses can bite, and all octopuses are technically venomous, no species that lives in South African waters is deadly. Still, I wanted to be prepared for what might happen if I *did* get nipped, so Mario flipped through the pages of our book to discover what kind of octopuses lay hidden in the ripples of water beneath us. Lo and behold, it was the common octopus, a wiggly, wobbly cephalopod whose bulging, oval head, eight sucker-lined arms, and piercing beady eyes make it look anything *but* common. Ranging from twelve to thirty-six inches in size, this squirmy, fast-moving creature lives in the warm and temperate waters of the Atlantic, Indian, and Pacific Oceans. They are both diurnal and nocturnal, and hunt using their scissorlike beaks to cut through the shells of other mollusks, or their drill-like radulae to bore into the armor of crustaceans, paralyzing them with nonlethal venom. When the shells are breached, an octopus pulls apart its prey with its tentacles and dines on the innards.

This particular octopus was hiding under a rock ledge, so I knew I had to come up with a plan to safely get it out. At this point, I'd already let the klipfish and crab loose; the top priority here was the octopus. I steadied myself above the pool and slowly dipped the net under its surface. I snuck my hand around the crevice of the rock, moving it ever so slightly in hopes of coaxing the octopus toward another, smaller pocket of the tide pool. The octopus shifted, carefully inching away from my intruding hand. I was expecting a more dynamic burst of movement, so I edged my hand closer, and—just like that—it squirted away! Where was it? Luckily, Mark spotted it making an escape out the back side of the pool!

"Dude, do you see it?" he said breathlessly, pointing just behind me. "Right there, right there, right there!"

Without me even realizing it, the octopus had slithered between a series of rocks over to the smaller pocket of the tide pool, just as I'd hoped! I spun around, grabbed my net, scooped…and…I had it!

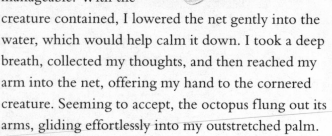

YES, YES, YES! I couldn't believe my luck! This specimen was the perfect size octopus for a handheld presentation; at just around a foot in length, it was slippery but manageable. With the creature contained, I lowered the net gently into the water, which would help calm it down. I took a deep breath, collected my thoughts, and then reached my arm into the net, offering my hand to the cornered creature. Seeming to accept, the octopus flung out its arms, gliding effortlessly into my outstretched palm.

There's a misconception about octopuses that they're sticky, as if they'll glue themselves to you with the suckers lining the bottom of their tentacles. While they can pry apart the shells of mollusks with these powerful tools, or adhere to slick rocks as they maneuver in their environment, they're surprisingly ineffective when they land on human hands, providing only a soft grip. The octopus is fast and slippery, and their tentacles move like the treads of a bulldozer in a perfectly fluid, unified motion. As I shifted the little beast from one hand to the other, this amazing slime ball slithered and slinked so much that I struggled to keep hold of it. The last thing I wanted to do was stress the animal, so I placed it in a shallow pool where it would

be completely contained. While I wanted to keep it hydrated, I was really hoping that the octopus would morph into the rock and algae around it, like a chameleon of the sea—and it did! Almost immediately, the texture of its skin went from glassy to bumpy, and from solid dark brown to dappled with tan and green, like the pebbles of sand and lichen beneath it. The transformation was incredible, and the octopus became nearly invisible as we watched it pump water through the valves in its head. It was clear that this animal wanted to stay hidden, hoping that its nonpredatory admirers would soon lose sight of it and walk away, disinterested.

After we observed it explore its environment, groping around the puddles and weeds, I lifted up the octopus gently. My mind started racing. *Please don't bite me. Please don't bite me,* I kept saying to myself. Even though I knew the venom of this species is nearly ineffectual, I still didn't want to take a bite from that piercing beak! After delivering a few more relevant facts while the octopus slid around in my hands like Jell-O, we decided it was time to say good-bye.

As I submerged my GoPro underwater, I also lowered the octopus back into the tide pool, capturing on video the send-off everyone had hoped for…*Psssst…pow!* A blast of ink! That's right; the coolest defense mechanism an octopus has is the ability to shoot a thick, foul-tasting spray of black liquid toward a pursuer as it darts away, making a hasty escape! This ink stings the attacker's eyes and obscures its vision, giving the cephalopod ample time to find a new place to hide. What a perfect ending to an unexpected encounter!

We'd thought the day had wrapped up, but little did we know that something even more exciting was still in store. Just moments later, the tide-pool creature I had always dreamed of encountering was about to reveal itself. Coyote Peterson was going to go hand-to-fin with a real-life shark!

Let's back up a little first. Ever since I was a kid, I've been completely and totally obsessed with sharks. I fell in love with *Jaws* when I was only six years old! My mom and I used to curl up on the couch, pop in the VHS tape, and sound out the timeless theme song as we fast-forwarded through all the setup and dialogue right to the shark scenes. When the shark's gaping, mammoth jaws opened, revealing rows of terrifying, knifelike teeth, my mom would hit PAUSE, and I'd squeal with delight. I'd lift a piece of paper to the glass and start tracing the outline of the shark through the flicker of the TV screen, finishing it later at my desk with my box of one hundred twenty crayons. I would do this over and over; my never-ending quest to make the perfect great white shark picture!

At this point in my career as an animal adventurer, I'd seen sharks in aquariums, but I'd never had the chance to touch one, much less catch one out in the wild. The possibility of seeing one in a tide pool always lingered in the back of my mind, but I had my doubts that it would ever happen. After all, how many times in life do your craziest dreams *actually* come true?

I'm here to tell you: If you expect the unexpected and believe anything is possible, they *will* come true!

After the inky send-off with the octopus, Mark and I decided to record a handful of cinematic B-roll shots that would capture the great expanse of the coastline as we made our way back to the vehicle. We sent Mario ahead with some of the unneeded camera gear, as filming these types of shots requires only two people and is usually the *only* time the team splits up. Ironically, as fate would have it, this is always when the rarest moments present themselves.

As I cautiously navigated the slick, craggy rocks, I wasn't paying any particular attention to the tide pools. We had already wrapped filming what we thought was the most epic creature we would come across. Instead, I was busy admiring and filming the scenery while navigating the hour-long trek back down the coastline toward civilization.

Noticing a shift in the tide, I paused to adjust my camera to capture one last shot of the beautiful tide pools and sprays of ocean surf. The waves were rolling back in as the tide began to rise, and salty water burst in every direction with each crash against the cliff side. Low tide had long passed, and before we knew it, our window for safe—or maybe just dry—passage back to base camp was narrowing. This is your sign that it's time to call it a day and head back toward high ground. I was catching a shot of the incoming waves shattering against the rocks, when, suddenly, I heard Mark's voice shaking with disbelief and a distinct ring of excitement.

"Oh my gosh...a shark."

What? I couldn't believe my ears! I turned to my left, in the direction of Mark's pointed finger, cast my gaze into a deeper pool, and set my sights on the unbelievable. My brain scrambled in bewilderment. The only statement I could muster was the exact same phrase Mark had just delivered!

"Oh my gosh…a shark." I looked up at Mark, both of us staring with looks of utter astonishment.

There it was: mini-*Jaws* lying peacefully at the bottom of its watery realm. This shark was small, flat, and gray, with two rounded, triangular fins that poked out on either side of its narrow body. Two smaller fins extended out and back near its long tail. I gawked at the animal as it swam in a tight, perfect circle, just barely disturbing the pebbles as it glided over the sandy bottom. As I regained my composure, I realized that this could be the episode of a lifetime! Not only would I fulfill my childhood dream of catching a shark, this would be a pivotal leap forward for the Brave Wilderness channel.

"Get Mario!" Mark said, snapping out of his stupor.

Mario was nowhere in sight! He could have been thirty minutes away by foot, and he had our precious, all-important field guide. Without it, we had no clue what kind of shark we were dealing with. And let's not forget to mention the fact that he also had the additional camera gear required to film a proper segment!

How were we going to get Mario back?! Mark and I were in such a remote location that the chances of us reaching him by phone were very slim. I looked down and saw that my phone had one bar of signal that flickered on and off. The success of this episode now depended on my fickle phone service, but I had to try. The ring tone crackled a few times, and then finally I heard a familiar voice on the other end of the line. *YES! He picked up!*

"Mario!" I screamed. "Dude…we found a shark!"

In the years Mario and I have worked together, he's come to expect a myriad of crazy things, but a shark in a South African tide pool was *not* one of them. "You did not find a shark," he said incredulously. "We've been to countless tide pools, and never—not once—have we seen a shark."

"Mario, I am not kidding; this is the real deal. I'm looking down into the water right now. It's a shark! Grab the cameras, and definitely bring the field guide. Follow the coastline back, and you can't miss us!"

When Mario joined us just ten minutes later, he was out of breath. He'd sprinted down the coast, under the rocky tunnel, and past the cliffs. Finally, the three of us stared down into the gaping tide pool—twenty feet across—and took in the magnificent oddity that lay still at the bottom of the water in front of us.

This small gray shark was just over two feet long. Its round snout sloped down over its mouth, and we could discern two sleepy, golden eyes on either side of its head. Mario pulled out the field guide, and we analyzed the shark's black spots as well as its dorsal and tail fin structure. We quickly came to the conclusion that it was spotted gully shark. Also called the sharptooth houndshark, this animal typically lives in groups in the warm, inshore waters of South Africa and Angola. They can be found in shallow, sandy beds, kelp forests, and coral reefs, hunting for crustaceans, small fish (including other sharks), and cephalopods. As full-grown adults, these sharks can measure

about five and a half to six feet in length, so the shark we saw before us must have been a juvenile.

My thoughts were racing, trying to come up with the best way to approach the shark. If I reached in and grabbed quickly, it could startle and respond aggressively. I knew its teeth were small—used for crushing and grinding shells rather than puncturing and ripping apart meat as a great white does—but I was still aware that the shark could mash my finger if I got too close to its mouth. The shark was definitely too big for my net, so the best way to approach it was to use my instincts and experience, and get in the water. I stepped down into the pool, the water only reaching as high as my knees, and I bent at the waist to get a closer look at my target. *You've wanted to do this your whole life, Coyote, so go for it!*

I took a deep breath and calmly submerged my right hand, then my left, as I steadily reached toward the shark. To my surprise, as my hands approached, it stayed still. Slowly, I wrapped my right hand around the shark, near the tail, and gently guided it toward the surface as my left hand supported the middle of its body. I'd done it! I was holding a shark with my bare hands! It wasn't slick and slimy, like the octopus, but instead was rough like sandpaper, allowing me to easily get a good grip. The shark was unbelievably calm, barely twitching at all as I lifted its head up, revealing its white belly to the cameras. It's almost as if the animal understood that I wasn't a threat, and somehow knew that one of my childhood dreams was to get up close and personal with a shark.

Like the Lake Erie water snake and countless other biting or stinging creatures I've met in the last few years, the shark is one of the most misunderstood species in the world. Despite all the panic surrounding shark sightings near shore, these animals kill an average of only *four* humans annually, and nearly all these attacks are a result of mistaken identity. Guess how many sharks are killed each year by shark-fin hunters or terrified boaters? Or die when they're caught up in fishing lines and nets? *TENS OF MILLIONS.* Unfortunately, overfishing has driven spotted gully sharks close to being declared a threatened species. The fact is, sharks play an incredibly important role in the health and sustainability of the marine ecosystem. Without them, different species of fish that feed on coral, kelp, or krill would become over populated, decimating the oceans resources. People who fear these magnificent animals, perceiving them as only bloodthirsty killers, have contributed to their vast, widespread destruction. Ever since I was a kid, I've wanted to help others see how special sharks really are. So this episode furthered my respect and affection for this creature and was a great start toward that goal.

The tide was rising quickly, and time was of the essence. I could have spent hours admiring the spotted gully shark, but the shark needed to be released before the conditions became any more dangerous. Besides, this was not an animal that could stay out of the water or be handled for an extensive amount of time. We realized that there was a much bigger pool with deeper pockets about ten feet away, so I gently grasped this exceptional

little shark, lifted it up, and quickly carried it in that direction. When the tide washes in, it has a tendency to be rather turbulent, so placing the shark in a larger and deeper pool would ensure it was not tossed around and injured.

I stepped knee-deep into the crystal-clear water of the tide pool and gently placed the shark beneath the surface. For a moment, it just lay in my hands, acclimating to the water around it and soaking in the nutrients flowing through its gills. Then, with a whip of its powerful tail, the shark thrust forward and gracefully swam off into the current. As I watched the shark's silhouette gradually disappear into the mixture of light and shadows, I smiled gratefully, knowing that this was going to make one incredible episode!

Catching both an octopus *and* my first shark still hails as the most epic and unexpected encounter that has ever happened to me on a tide pool adventure. Interacting with these animals was a true honor, and the memories I carry from that incredible day still fill me with wonder. Encountering these marvelous animals was purely a matter of chance; we found ourselves in the right place at the right time. With tide pools, you never know what you are going to come across, and that is what makes exploring them so much fun!

Chapter Three
Dangerous Caiman Catch!

Chapter 3 / Dangerous Caiman Catch!

I've felt as if I've been striving for the impossible in so many of my greatest adventures—whether it was tracking a bear in the wilds of Alaska, coming face-to-face with a shadow stalker in the Costa Rican rain forest, or coming arm-to-stinger with the most infamous creature on the insect sting pain index: the Executioner wasp. Each of these encounters had an element of danger, and while preparing for them, I couldn't shake my trepidation about interacting with these ferocious individuals. But facing your fears, and then conquering them, can lead to the most exciting experiences of your life! With great risk comes even greater reward, and for me, that has never been more true than the time I traveled to a remote area of Costa Rica to track down a reptile I'd dreamed about catching my entire life: the spectacled caiman!

Like sharks, snapping turtles, and the elusive wolverine—an apex predator you'll read about later in this book—the spectacled caiman is a creature I've been obsessed with since I was a just a kid. I used to subscribe to something called *Zoobooks*, a colorful children's magazine where each issue featured photographs, illustrations, diagrams, and fun activities, all centered on one particular group of animals. I'd wait patiently for the mailman to arrive with my copy of *Zoobooks* every month, and the second I held it in my hands, I'd sprint into my bedroom, shut the door, and study it from cover to cover. With my head full of facts and figures—and a pullout poster of the month's feature animal fresh on my wall—I'd stay in my room for hours, imagining what it would be like to get up close and personal with some of nature's most awe-inspiring beasts.

One of my favorite issues of *Zoobooks* featured the spectacled caiman, a small yet fierce member of the order Crocodilia. Now, some of you might be confused about the various reptiles that we call crocodilians, and some of you may have never even heard of a caiman. Allow me to explain! The term *crocodilian* encompasses various species of crocodiles, alligators, caimans, and gharials. For the sake of convenience, many people just use the term *crocodiles*; however, true crocodiles have unique characteristics, differentiating them from their aquatic cousins. Just as you wouldn't call all colorful, tropical birds *parrots*, you wouldn't call all scaly aquatic reptiles *crocodiles*!

The spectacled caiman, also called the common caiman, is one of several species of the genus *caiman*, and their super-unique structure always made them my favorite crocodilian. With boney ridges protruding above their eyes, this reptile looks as if they're wearing a set of old-timey horn-rimmed spectacles. While they're usually a dull olive green, their skin often darkens when temperatures turn cold. Their seventy-five conical teeth are crazy-looking: sharp, jagged, and widely spaced, the upper teeth often extend over the lower jaw, and the lower middle teeth sometimes stick out over the upper jaw. More than any other crocodilian, these chompers cause spectacled caimans to look even more like dinosaurs, and—to me—that made them even cooler. Once fully grown, an adult can reach a maximum length of about eight feet and tip the scales at over eighty pounds. This is significantly smaller than a full-grown American alligator or crocodile, but make no mistake—their reduced stature doesn't mean they're any less intimidating. Caimans are perfectly evolved predators, and wield a muscular jaw capable of exerting a bite force of up to one thousand five hundred pounds per square inch. That's about ten times more powerful than the bite force of a human, and easily more powerful than an adult male lion! Spectacled caiman are ruthless and intimidating predators that I've often referred to as the "bulldogs of the crocodile world."

It was during the winter of 2017 when we took our trip deep into the Costa Rican rain forest. Our adventure began in a small village on the banks of the beautifully remote Sierpe River. We'd planned the expedition with the help of a herpetologist named Roel de Plecker, who'd assembled a team that would assist us on our epic quest to catch the spectacled caiman. In this particular river system, we could expect to find two kinds of crocodilians—the American crocodile and the spectacled caiman—but our aim for this episode was only the latter. If we managed to locate a good-size specimen, we hoped to catch it using a method known as safe snaring. This would allow us to get the powerful reptile safely under control and onto our research boat for the purpose of collecting valuable biometric data—body measurement and physical observations—before releasing the animal back into the wild.

Spectacled caimans live in wetlands and rivers all over Central America and northern South America, so while we knew that wrangling one would be challenging, finding one seemed like it would be fairly straightforward. "There are caimans everywhere," Roel confirmed, "so we should have no problem spotting one. The rare ones are actually the crocodiles."

Because our target species was nocturnal, mainly active while hunting at night, we would have to film this episode without the advantage of daylight. When caimans attack, they are merciless and opportunistic, ambushing animals that swim in or come to drink from the shallow waters near shore. For a juvenile caiman, small fish, frogs, snakes, snails, crustaceans, and

mollusks are all fair game. Larger, fully grown caiman are a little more voracious, with their recorded diets including over one hundred species. Like their larger cousins, they will spring up from the water or scurry down the shoreline to snatch up small mammals like raccoons or wild pigs. Then, using their strong jaws, pointed teeth, and robust bodies, they shake and crush their prey before swallowing it whole. Caimans can also jump. Yes, you read that right! This amazing reptile can propel half of its body from the murky water into the air, extending its gaping, snaggletoothed jaws up and over tree branches. Once airborne, they snap down on young herons, egrets, or other water birds, and plunge back into the water, where they finish their meal. All in all, this is one incredibly agile and perfectly evolved ambush predator. So I think it's pretty easy to understand why this reptile has always fascinated me!

Our actual voyage wouldn't be much different than a *Jurassic*–esque quest into the deepest part of the jungle, searching for a creature that most men would never lay eyes on. The slow-moving Sierpe River twists through the southwest part of Costa Rica, spilling into the Pacific Ocean after only fifty miles. Its depth and width change with the seasons and tides, but the Sierpe can never be crossed with mere waders. Remote and tranquil, it boasts the largest reserve of mangroves in all Costa Rica, and is lined with lush, populated rain forests packed with thousands of Costa Rica's native wildlife. High above its murky waters, scarlet macaws can be heard cackling, morpho butterflies flutter by, and howler monkeys and three-toed sloths recline in the branches of the surrounding trees. Near its muddy banks lie venomous fer-de-lance vipers, guinea-pig-size rodents named agoutis, and mighty American crocodiles—who we never expected to see.

We had an energetic team made up of me, Roel, Mark, Mario, and two additional crew members who would operate the boat. Our trusty vessel was called the *Spider*. It was a seasoned, motorized deck boat—painted white and light green—that could easily handle the long night of searching ahead of us. On board, there was a long bench lining the inside, a weatherproof soft top to protect us from rain, and plenty of floor space to stash our gear. Taking my place on the bench beside Mario, I put the finishing touches on the most important tool of the night: my pole snare.

Our poles were made from long pieces of bamboo, duct tape, rope, and looped wire at the end that made up the snare. I've used these tools several times before, but tonight I had the chance to construct and test my own. The mechanics of a pole snare are efficient and simple: I'd extend the pole toward the caiman, lasso the snare around its snout and head, and then let the loop slip down to its thick, muscular neck. When the crocodilian inevitably began to thrash, trying its best to escape, the snare would tighten and break away from the pole, exposing a long line of rope that I'd then hold on to as I attempted to wrangle the animal. Now, in regard to the safety of the spectacled caiman, let me assure you: No harm would come to the reptile—the wire was coated in clear pliable rubber. There was no way it could cut the crocodilian with the pressure I was able to exert on the line. Keep in mind that this reptile's neck is not only solid muscle, but also armored with scales. No matter how dramatic the struggle may become, the rubber-coated snare would be the safest method for both the caiman and for us.

The sun made its descent, its pink and orange arms spreading across the surface of the tranquil river, and I reflected on the personal importance of this trip. When I was a kid, my nose buried in a copy of *Zoobooks*, I imagined myself as a rugged explorer, heading out into the wilds of the great unknown to search for an elusive crocodilian. Swarmed by mosquitoes, I'd listen to the sound of my boat cutting quietly through reptile-infested rivers as I scanned the distance with my binoculars, hoping my eyes would land on the ultimate prize: the spectacled caiman!

As the last rays of light cast a warm glow on the riverbanks, our captain moved toward the back of the boat and topped off the engine. Mario and I tested our snares, Mark secured our cameras and packs, and the crew made a few final adjustments before pulling the cord. When I heard the unmistakable sounds of a sputtering motor, I felt my nerves flare to life like a jolt of electricity. Before we knew it, we had pulled away from the dock and were steadily puttering down the river. We were off!

Caimans bask on muddy slides that extend down from the banks of the river into the water. So, under the last glow of light, we headed several miles down the main channel of the river and into some of its narrow offshoots, scouring the shore for eye shine glinting in the light of our flashlights. Our plan was to spot a caiman lurking close to shore, motor the boat toward it, cross our fingers that we wouldn't startle it, and cut the engine, letting the boat drift into the mud and stop. I'd then grab the pole snare and lean out, lassoing the caiman while the boat was safely beached on land. After the muscle-bound beast was under control, we'd haul it to the side of the boat, lift up its snout, and tape it shut with electrical tape. Then we'd grab its front legs and hoist the reptile onto the boat, where we'd collect its biometric data. Sounds easy, right?

It wasn't. Our problems started right away.

"Over there, over there! I see some eye shine!" I whispered to Roel, who was aiming his flashlight into the mangroves while Mark and Mario filmed.

"Nah, sorry, Coyote. That's a small crocodile," Roel replied.

"Man!" I said. "If we could just find a caiman of that size, it would be perfect!"

I'm not kidding when I say this same scenario unfolded another twenty times over the next four hours. One of us would see eye shine reflecting off the glare of the flashlight, I'd feel

a surge of adrenaline course through my body, and then Roel
would sigh and shake his head. "Sorry, that's another crocodile."
Foiled again! Along the branches of towering trees, we spotted
night herons, scarlet macaws, and swallows. In the tangled
arches of the mangroves, we identified boa constrictors and bird
snakes. Surrounding us were swarms of mosquitoes and streaks
of hungry bats, gorging themselves overhead. We even saw
several American crocodiles—supposedly rare in this river—
watching as we cruised by. But no spectacled caimans.

This reptile that I valued above all was supposed to be
everywhere! The whole group was bewildered. Earlier, Roel
had assured us that we'd see *dozens* of caimans and next to no

crocodiles, yet the opposite was happening! There wasn't a spectacled caiman in sight, and there was absolutely nothing we could do about it. We had prepared to the best of our abilities, following the guidance of experts from the area, but sometimes it really does come down to luck, the only thing we were lacking up to that point.

The night wore on, and after many hours of searching, the captain decided to shut off the outboard motor, letting the boat drift.

"We need to head back," he said. "We're going to run out of gas if we don't."

For a split second, I was disappointed, and then I realized that all hope was not lost. The trip up the river had reached its inevitable end, but the voyage back gave us equal opportunity to locate our target. I took a deep breath, cast my doubts overboard, and lifted up my flashlight to continue scanning the muddy banks for eye shine. Another forty minutes passed as the boat hummed steadily through the water, and again and again, we only saw crocodiles. Probably the same crocodiles from before, all grinning at us, aware that they were completely safe from the snare skills of Coyote Peterson. Then, suddenly, one of the crew members nudged me. "I've got eye shine up out of the water and tucked back into that thicket of bamboo."

Out of the water and tucked back on land?! This was highly unusual! The crocodilians in this river network are known to stick close to the muddy slides so they can slip into the water at a moment's notice to attack their prey or escape a potential predator. Why in the world would one be tucked back into a thick, tangled mess of bamboo?

There's only one way to find out, I thought.

"Cut the motor!" the crew member whispered to the captain, and the propeller fell silent. We began slowly drifting toward the shore, one flashlight's beam still fixed on the two glowing eyes that stared us down. I could feel the suspense mounting as we got closer. *It's not another crocodile. I can feel it!* I felt the tug of the muddy bank on the bottom of the boat as we reached solid ground and slid to a stop. I peered through the reeds at the bright-red eye shine glaring back at me, and knew we'd hit gold. There were the distinctive ridges on the top of the reptile's head. It was a spectacled caiman!

This incredible predator was hunkered down a solid ten feet back from the shore in a tangled mess of bamboo. I did some mental calculations about how I might catch him from inside the boat and realized that the bamboo pole I held would get me only six feet closer to my target. Keeping safety in mind, I searched my brain for a solution. The stiff stalks of bamboo were definitely a hazard, but I had never felt so determined.

You're on the adventure of a lifetime, Coyote, I said to myself. *You're just a few yards away from a creature you've been waiting your whole life to catch. Making your dreams come true is a challenge, and that challenge involves risks. So go brave...or go home!*

"Hold this, hold this, hold this," I whispered to Mario as I handed him the pole snare. Then, not letting myself worry for a moment about the fact that a hungry crocodile might be lurking below us, I swung my legs off the bow of the boat, and silently slid into the water.

It was time to go face-to-snout with a spectacled caiman!

Upon entering the water, my legs immediately began sinking into sticky mud on the river's basin. This was bad… really bad. My mobility was very limited, and I was situated between the caiman and the river—my only escape. Talk about a rock and hard place! I turned back toward Mario and signaled for him to hand me the pole snare. I reached up and closed my hand around the pole, not taking my eyes off the statuesque reptile; it hadn't moved an inch. Even with all the lights, the reptile still felt as if it were hidden. Except for a low hum of insects, the scene was so quiet, you could have heard a pin drop. With all the strength in my legs, I resisted the mud's steady suction, trying my best to not make a sound that would startle

the reptile and send it hurtling for the safety of the river, which I was currently blocking.

I turned my head for a split second and noticed that the rest of the crew was now staring down into the water. *Oh great, they're looking for crocodiles*, I realized, *because American crocodiles are known to silently sneak in toward land to attack their prey.* I was right in the danger zone, but Coyote Peterson was not going to be a crocodile's dinner tonight, so I had to make my move!

With gritted teeth, I fought a final step closer and decided this was it. I extended the bamboo pole out toward the caiman's snout with focused precision, when, all of a sudden, *boom!* The reptile shot forward like a bolt of lightning and straight into the snare!

"I've got it!" I yelled. "I've got the back of its body, and it's really slippery!"

This crocodilian had catapulted itself right into the snare trap, and the wire had gone over its head, down its body, and over one of its legs. It didn't thrash around at first, remaining impressively still with the snare wedged awkwardly around its belly. I held the rope tightly in my hands, and as I forced myself into the reeds, trying to get the caiman, it lunged again.

I could see its round, beady golden eyes looking toward the boat, and I wondered what it was thinking. Was it calculating its ability to move out of the bamboo thicket and slide down the muddy embankment into the river, or was it timing its next lunge to break free of the haphazard snare? The rope was getting tangled between the stalks of bamboo and my arms, and I was running out of good positions to make the final grab. The caiman was growing impatient and began thrashing wildly with its three loose feet, mouth agape, emitting threatening hisses from its throat. *Sssssssssss!* It lunged toward me and, quick as a cat, I dodged, letting the rope fall to the ground, finally getting in position behind it. Then I snatched up the line, now untangled from the stalks of bamboo, and regained control over the caiman.

"You got a shot?" I called to Mark. With my body in position, I planted my feet firmly in the mud, gathered my wits about me, and prepared to pounce. "One...two...three!" Hands at the ready and arms outstretched, I launched my body onto it, not even thinking about the fact that I could have impaled myself on a piece of bamboo.

"I *got it*!" I screamed. "Holy mackerel!" I'd landed right on top of the caiman, and its thick, scaly skin and muscular torso were just as impressive as I'd imagined! I grasped my hands firmly around its neck, just behind its brick-like head, and pressed down with all the weight of my upper body as the caiman tried to resist. I could feel its immense strength under me, and I scooted forward, pinning its legs and chest under my weight, gaining the advantage I knew I needed.

"I'm gonna need your help, Mario," I said. Mario had already jumped into the water and come up on land just after me. I couldn't risk the caiman grabbing my hand or my arm with its crooked teeth, and although I had a degree of control over it, it still took all of my strength and concentration to keep it that way. If it got ahold of me, the animal's natural instinct would be to shake violently from side to side. Without question, my limb would be shredded to pieces, and I'd be one hand lighter.

Luckily, Mario was by my side. "I need you to wrap its snout." I positioned my hand just behind its eyes as Mario reached in and gently closed them. Crocodilians will stay calm if their eyes are closed, so this allowed me to immediately reposition my hands from the neck. I grasped its snout and held it closed. It's a dangerous move, but Mario and I pulled it off with expert precision, and I wrapped my fingers around its jaws with a vicelike grip. With its sturdy jaws now firmly in my hands, Mario quickly wrapped black electrical tape around the snout, securing the mouth shut. Then he reached down toward the caiman's midsection, lifted the wire snare, and repositioned it along the reptile's hips.

Chapter 3 / Dangerous Caiman Catch!

BOOM! The creature seemed to be biding its time, because suddenly it exploded with energy, thrashing back and forth trying to break free of its predicament. The combination of the slick mud, the rope, the jagged pieces of bamboo, and the monstrous power of the caiman in my arms was too much for just me alone. It took both me and Mario to wrestle the rowdy reptile back from the water's edge. We couldn't gain the upper hand while it was off the ground, so on my knees, with my contender grappled in my arms, I twisted to my right and thrust the caiman back onto the soil, falling right on its back. After all of that, it relented, but we were both tangled up in the reeds all over again.

"I am lassoed together with a spectacled caiman!" I yelled. "This is unbelievably exciting. *WOW!*"

I was covered in mud and unsure of how I was going to get out of the bamboo and back to the boat, but I didn't care. I'd taken a risk—and reaped the reward. I successfully captured a spectacled caiman, and what a perfect specimen it was!

THWACK! "OW!" I grunted. For being relatively small compared to other crocodilians, this caiman was not going down easily. I couldn't take my weight off it for an instant, because as soon as I did, it headbutted me in another surge of the scuffles.

I decided that the best way to move the animal was to wiggle down the embankment with it underneath me. My weight was the only thing keeping it under control until we could get it up onto the boat. I lurched to my left, sliding down the mud until I was in perfect position. Then I wrapped my arms around the caiman's midsection, stood up, and hoisted it toward the boat, where Mario, also covered in mud, was now waiting to receive the reptile.

Mario quickly used all his own weight to pin down the animal, as it gave one last attempt to escape, and was able to successfully secure it just as I climbed up out of the mud and onto the boat myself. We had done it! The spectacled caiman was in the boat and ready to get up close for the cameras!

It took me a moment, but I finally caught my breath. I was covered in mud from head to toe—I looked like a swamp creature! The team and I were buzzing with excitement, high fives were being shared by all. I'd taken one of the biggest risks of my life, and I'd captured one of the animals I'd always dreamed of.

At just about five feet in length from its snout to the tip of its tail, this was one admirable caiman! We checked its eighteen long-clawed fingers and toes, looked at its earflaps, and inspected all its armor plating from the top of its head to the tip of its tail. I noticed the bony ridge on its back and how robust its skin and muscles felt, a sign that it was eating a healthy diet in a balanced ecosystem. Then I looked at its eyes.

"As compared to an alligator
or crocodile, the eyelids
are much more bony,"
I said, rubbing my
hand over the caiman's
head. Then I put my
finger on one of its eyelids.
"Watch this. Caiman have nictitating membranes. I'll close its
eye. Ready? One, two, three." I gently pushed down the eyelid,
and as it reopened, a filmy white membrane remained in place
for a fraction of a second, then slid across its eye sideways like a
windshield wiper. "Right there, check it out…see that? That's
the nictitating membrane. It stays like that when the caiman's
underwater to block any debris from the environment scraping
its eyeballs as it's moving about while hunting."

Marveling at this amazing beast I had in front of me, I
couldn't believe how perfect its scales were. Many caimans are
scarred up or missing an eye from territorial fights with other
predators of their habitat, but not this one. It was pretty much
flawless.

"The osteoderms are incredible," I said, referring to the
bony plates embedded in the reptile's skin. "The spectacled
caiman has more armored plating than the alligator or the
crocodile! And right here, specifically on the back of the neck, it
is solid muscle and solid bone."

If you were shooting photographs for a field guide, I thought, *this
would be the perfect example of a healthy adult spectacled caiman.*

We'd done our work collecting biometric data, but the inherent danger wasn't gone. We had to release the reptile back to the muddy banks, meaning I was going to have to leave the safety of our vessel once again. With the caiman grasped tightly in my arms, I carefully jumped from the boat onto the slippery bank. *Please stay calm*, I thought. *You're almost home.* I steadied myself, set down the reptile, and for the last time used my weight to pin it to the squishy ground. After I unbound its toothy snout and loosened the snare, I jumped back, letting it go. With one last, golden-eyed look in my direction, it slid down the mud and into the water. Then, with a thrust of its tail, the reptile exploded with power and disappeared into the murky water.

It was past 3:00 AM by the time we got back to the village. When I finally took off my boots and sat on my bed, I realized I'd never felt so satisfied—or muddy—in my life. I'd faced a challenge, acknowledged the risks before me, then looked—and leaped! Encountering and capturing the magnificent spectacled caiman was an old-school adventure on a grand scale, but I'd done it. I'd accomplished a dream by risking it all and taking a chance, catching one of the most impressive crocodilians in the world!

Chapter Four
Diving for Sea Turtles!

A ustralia's northeast coast is a sunny and tranquil place, where dry tropical trade winds rustle the palm trees, and the warm blue waters of the Coral Sea lap onto its sandy beaches. The small town of Bowen lies almost precisely on the center of Queensland's shoreline and in close proximity to the Great Barrier Reef. The world's largest coral system, the Great Barrier Reef is a breathtaking, sixteen thousand-mile-long natural habitat that's earned its rightful place as one of the seven natural wonders of the world. The reef is Earth's largest structure made entirely by living organisms, and its extraordinary biodiversity makes it home to giant clams, white-bellied sea eagles, blue starfish, and whitetip reef sharks to name a few. It's also home to the green sea turtle, an iconic reptile that the Brave Wilderness team flew in to see in March of 2017.

Growing up to five feet long and weighing between two hundred forty and four hundred fifty pounds, green sea turtles are one of the largest sea turtle species in the world. Named after the greenish-colored fat and cartilage that lies under their carapace, or top shell, this elegant reptile lives in the tropical and subtropical regions of oceans around the world. Green sea turtles in the Pacific, however, have unique characteristics and behaviors that differenciate them from those found in other regions. The specific type of sea turtle that we were searching for is called the Eastern Pacific green sea turtle. With their wide brownish-olive top shells, yellow-colored bottom shells, and kind, all-knowing eyes, these endangered reptiles are beloved by people around the world. While I'd always respected them,

I was about to find out how much I truly admired and adored these majestic creatures of the sea.

Most of you know that I've been fascinated with turtles my whole life, and I've made it my goal to catch bigger and bigger individuals on each of my turtle adventures. When I was a kid exploring the lakes and wetlands near my hometown in Ohio, I liked nothing more than to plunge my hands into the murky water and grab on to the spiked, algae-coated back of a snapping turtle, lifting it to the muddy embankment so I could appreciate its beastly, perfectly evolved form. To me, turtles have always been nature's most inspiring reptile. Their rounded shells protect their soft bodies like armor, and their sharp, curved claws extend out of their webbed feet like daggers. Holding and observing the fiercest snappers still fills me with a sense of wonder and amazement. When I look at one, I can see the raw instinct in its eyes contrasted with the gentleness of its movements—until it lurches its head toward me, threatening to take a bite! Whether on land or in water, turtles of all types are perfectly adapted to their environments, and I've continued to respect the seamless balance they strike in their natural habitats. In Hawaii, I had the remarkable opportunity to swim alongside these graceful giant sea turtles, admiring them from only a few yards away, but I'd never had a chance to get up close and personal with one—for good reason. It's against the law.

Sea turtles—especially green sea turtles—are the unfortunate victims of man's destruction of the natural environment. In some countries, these reptiles are hunted for food, and their eggs—which they lay on the beaches where they are born every two to four years—are often stolen. Nesting areas have been destroyed by overdevelopment and human encroachment. In addition, sea turtles often mistake trash floating in the water for food, and after eating it, they become ill and often pass away. Their nesting sites, once remote, isolated beaches, have become contaminated with artificial light, reducing the survival rate for hatchlings who need to follow the light of the moon to the sea. Their rapidly decreasing numbers have led to strict laws and heavy fines for getting too close. If you don't have the proper permits, it is absolutely illegal to touch a sea turtle, much less catch one. So, when the Brave Wilderness team and I decided we wanted to head to Australia to come hand-to-shell with a green sea turtle, we knew we had to find the right partners to make it happen.

Mario immediately reached out to the World Wildlife Fund of Australia, an influential wildlife and environmental conservation organization that partners with businesses, government, communities, and Indigenous groups to help protect Australia's most vulnerable native species. When Mario explained who we were and asked how we might set up a trip to catch green sea turtles—all for the purpose of helping to protect them, of course—the man he spoke with couldn't have been more helpful.

"You should talk to the Gudjuda Rangers," he said. "They're in Queensland, and they know everything about green sea turtles."

The Gudjuda Reference Group Aboriginal Corporation, also known as the Gudjuda Rangers, represents the Bindal, Juru, and Ngaro traditional owner groups. These men and women work to protect the land, sea, and animals. They help ensure the survival of the sea turtles who are native to the Queensland coast. Intimately connected to the ocean and the life in it, these sentinels of the sea have been granted permission by the Australian government to track, catch, tag, and monitor these cherished reptiles. They send their data off to scientists who then study it to determine turtle migration patterns, make sure a healthy balance of the sea is being maintained, and to mitigate human destruction of their habitats. The Rangers also conduct tours where you can watch them locate and tag these magnificent creatures, giving you a window into their conservation efforts. Naturally, I wanted much more than a nice, relaxing boat trip where I'd watch someone else catch a turtle. I had a big goal in mind, and when Mario reached out to them, he made that abundantly clear.

"Coyote wants to *catch* a sea turtle," he said, putting extra emphasis on the word. "He's caught hundreds of snapping turtles in his life, so I know he's got the skills to do it."

"I'm sure that's true," the Ranger answered, "but not just anybody can capture a turtle. He has to learn from us first."

And that, Coyote Pack, is a big lesson I learned on my quest for the timeless green sea turtle. Listening and learning is one of the keys to making your dreams come true. You may think you're the master of your particular domain—like I am with catching snapping turtles—but there's *always* more to learn, and there's *always* room to grow. Finding a great mentor who can help you set goals, challenge your assumptions, hone your craft, or teach you an entirely new skill set is invaluable on *your* quest to fulfill your wildest dreams. I was truly fortunate to find such a passionate and proficient guide when I traveled to Australia.

The trip from Columbus, Ohio, to Bowen, Queensland, was extreme, to say the least. We traveled for over twenty-four hours, taking two flights across the continental United States, followed by an exhausting flight over the Pacific Ocean, and then finally a flight up the eastern coast of the Land Down Under. I'd never been in transit for that long in my life. We were all first-time travelers to Australia, and greatly underestimated the grueling, disorienting impact jet lag can have. We never imagined that we'd need more than a day to recuperate. After what seemed like days of traveling, we hastily unpacked our bags and gear and settled into an unsound sleep at our hotel. Our alarm clocks going off at 6:00 AM felt like a slap in the face, but we pulled ourselves out of bed and walked out the door. After all, we had some Gudjuda Rangers to meet, and I had a green sea turtle to catch!

———

I could smell the salty ocean and feel the wind whipping a dry heat from the mainland as Mario, Mark, and I walked out on the dock to greet the Rangers who'd be taking us out on their boat. A Juru elder named James welcomed us first, performing a traditional smoke ceremony to wish us the best of luck on our voyage. Even though my head was spinning from jet lag, I felt a sense of peace as I watched him wave a small, flaming bucket out over the water. When the smoke passed my field of vision, I thought, *They're here to teach me, and I'm here to learn.*

Our plan was for me to shadow a man named Aaron Taiters, who was the most accomplished sea turtle catcher among the Rangers. Much as I'd mastered my technique of leaping from a kayak to pounce on a common snapping turtle, Aaron had mastered catapulting himself off a speeding boat and onto the backs of many green sea turtles. Knowing my experience and understanding that I was prepared to listen, Aaron was positive he could show me how to catch a turtle, and I was confident it wouldn't be too difficult. *Right?* What I never anticipated was just how fast sea turtles can swim!

Despite their mass, green sea turtles can swim through the water at speeds up to thirty-five miles per hour. Think about it: The fastest human running speed is only twenty-eight miles per hour. Thirty-five miles per hour is about as fast as your car driving down a busy urban road, or how quickly most accomplished skiers rocket down a steep slope. As green sea turtles move their paddle-like flippers in long, powerful strokes, water glides over their heart-shaped, streamlined shells. They cut through the ocean like torpedoes.

Chapter 4 / Diving for Sea Turtles!

Standing on the edge of our speeding motor boat with Aaron, scanning just below the surface for turtles, I couldn't believe my eyes when we saw our first one. It was lightning-fast! I'd just assumed these turtles would be meandering along, lazily searching for some sea grass or algae to munch on. But, no, these creatures were reptilian speeding bullets. I was starting to understand how difficult this would be!

"It's not easy," Aaron said. "You have to dive ahead of the turtle with your hands out. That way, as it swims forward under you, you can grab on to the front of its shell, and it'll take you with it."

Wow, I said to myself. *This was going to be very different than catching a snapping turtle!* My tried-and-true technique for catching a snapping turtle is to grab on to the *back* of the shell so the turtle can't swing its body around to bite me. If I was in front of a sea turtle, how could I trust that they wouldn't swim into me and knock me out?

I'd just have to learn from Aaron! Following the path of the fast-moving turtle, our driver, Eddie, whipped the boat around, right to left as the reptile changed its course, trying to escape us. I noticed this one was smaller than average for a green turtle, but that didn't matter. I was Aaron's eager apprentice, and I was about to watch him dive into the sea and grab one with his bare hands!

Whoosh! Aaron leaped from the speeding boat with his arms out in front of him and dove into the water with a giant *SPLASH!* Eddie killed the boat's engine, and I watched eagerly to see if Aaron would come to the surface with a turtle in his arms. When he appeared a few seconds later, he didn't have a smile on his face—or a green sea turtle anywhere near him. Even experts come up short sometimes, and Aaron had miscalculated where the sea turtle was, landing just behind it when he hit the water.

This same scenario happened a few times over the next few hours, and by the time lunch rolled around, I was wondering if Aaron's miraculous sea turtle–catching powers were the stuff of fiction. Not just that, but I was worried I wasn't going to make it to the end of the day! It was 2:00 in the morning in my brain, and I'd spent half the day actively scanning the choppy waters, blinding light reflecting off the waves as I stared beneath them, trying to detect dark shadows moving beneath the surface. The sun was now high in the sky, beating relentlessly down and baking me in my wet suit. I was starting to shut down, occasionally getting so dizzy that I had to steady myself by holding on to the boat's railing so I didn't fall face first into the sea. All I could think about was taking a long snooze, but I constantly reminded myself that I was here to learn, and we were going to catch a sea turtle if it was the last thing we ever did! So when Eddie started up the boat engine after a brief lunch, I felt a jolt of enthusiasm down my spine as I imagined the task before us.

The boat zipped through the water as Aaron and I stared down into it, hoping to see a shadow. Suddenly, something the size of a dining room table appeared out of nowhere. Was it a

massive stingray? No! A rock? We saw flippers, so no, it was not!

"It's a huge turtle," Aaron said with excitement, "and I am going to show you how it's done."

The turtle veered to the right, but Eddie was hot on its trail. He cut the boat toward the speedy reptile, throwing me off balance. After a few turbulent moments where we thought we'd lost it, Eddie maneuvered the boat next to the elegant creature. Aaron looked up briefly, then nodded. With his arms outstretched, he dove from the boat…and disappeared!

Let me back up for a moment. In some of the areas we'd been exploring, the water had been shallow, but the area we'd found ourselves in at this particular moment was deep. When Aaron dove into the water, he fully submerged himself, knowing the turtle was going to dive, too. Had he caught the reptilian beast? We eagerly watched the water as the waves rolled over the location where Aaron dove in. Time was ticking by, and he still had not resurfaced!

"Help him!" Eddie shouted, and I sprang into action, leaping into the water. Mario immediately followed, swimming toward me as we watched Aaron and the turtle rise to the surface. Oh my gosh! This was the biggest sea turtle I'd ever seen in my life!

This regal reptile's short beak—which is round, rather than hooked like a snapping turtle's—was curled down ever so slightly in a snarl. The turtle stared me right in the eyes as if it had a sinister plot in mind. Then it lunged forward, opened its mouth, and chomped down right on to Mario's wet suit,

pinching only the neoprene and narrowly missing his arm!
The lower beak of a sea turtle is jagged and serrated, and I
knew that they were capable of tearing into flesh. Mario was
very lucky. Thinking fast, I grabbed on to Mario's other arm,
and altogether—me, Mario, the turtle, and Aaron on top of
it—formed an awkward human chain powered by the weighty
reptile on whom our lives depended. The turtle shifted its body
forward and attempted to dive, plunging us into what very
well might have been our breaking point. At almost the same
time, the boat slid up next to us, and Eddie threw a few ropes
overboard to us.

"Grab on to them!" he yelled.

Still solidly planted on the turtle's back, Aaron reached
for the ropes and placed them loosely and delicately around
the turtle's front flippers. We held on for dear life as Eddie
maneuvered slowly toward shallower water. Less than a minute
later, we could finally stand up, and the turtle opened its mouth
and let go of Mario's wet suit.

"Dude, that's probably the craziest catch I've ever made,"
Aaron said as a second boat came up next to us. It was the
research vessel, and it was equipped to hoist the turtle up so the
Rangers could collect the turtle's valuable biometric data.

When the turtle was safely onboard, I couldn't believe
the sight before me. This revered reptile's shell was smooth
and solid, marbled green and brown, and flecked with dots of
yellow. I admired the animal's sentient, peaceful eyes, tucked
into a rounded head that, unlike other turtles, doesn't retract

into its shell. The Rangers soon
determined we'd caught a male,
and I admired this resplendent
gentleman's jagged, pointy tail, which
was longer and thicker than my forearm. Then
we weighed him. At 293 pounds, he was a whopper,
the second-biggest turtle the Gudjuda Rangers had
ever caught! It was true: Aaron *was* the master, and
I was grateful to be, at least for the moment, his right-hand man.

Now it was time for Coyote Peterson to catch a turtle!

After we released the massive beast back into the sea,
making sure his identification tag was secure and his biometric
data logged in the record books, our boat set off again. Staying
in the shallow water, we quickly spotted another one. The
turtle's wide carapace and oar-like flippers moved fluidly just
under the surface. *This is it, Coyote,*
I said to myself as I made sure my
GoPro was firmly attached to my
wet suit just before I pressed
RECORD. *You've learned from the
best, and now it's all up to you.*
I calculated how far forward I
needed to jump, crouched down ever
so slightly so I could get some air, and
leaped off the moving boat!

My arms and head sliced into the water, and for a moment,
I lost my bearings. At this point, I wasn't wearing a dive mask,

and since I wear contact lenses, I had to close my eyes the moment I hit the water or they'd wash out. I couldn't see a thing, but I could feel a gentle pressure under me, and I moved my hands toward something solid, grabbing on to whatever it was beneath me. *It's a flipper!* I realized, and I closed my fingers over it, marveling at its smooth leathery texture and sturdy, muscular girth. This front flipper was slippery, though, and it slid right through my hand as quickly as I'd grabbed on to it. I rose to the surface, realizing I'd been defeated. *Argh!*

Then, almost as if it were planned, Aaron leaped from the bow of the boat into the water, and right on top of the turtle to make the catch! All the disappointment I'd felt melted away as I realized we still caught the turtle. If that wasn't teamwork, I don't know what is.

The research boat returned, and we once again helped lift the turtle onto the boat so the Rangers could collect its data. This turtle was a female and although not as large as the last one we'd caught, she was still an impressive specimen. Once the necessary data was logged, we sat with her for a moment, silently admiring her beauty, before returning her to the sea. I'd try a few more catches that afternoon—all misses—but as the sun began to dip in the sky, it was time to head back. Eddie steered us home to shore, and we closed the book on day one of our sea-turtle adventure.

———

Jet lag is a terrible beast that does everything it can to deny you precious sleep. I tossed and turned all night, remembering the feeling of the turtle's front flipper in my hand, slipping just out of my grasp. With my head in a constant fog, I started to feel defeated, wondering if either exhaustion or lack of confidence would get the best of me. But then I remembered Aaron's careful critiques, his wise mentoring, and the incredibly perceptive way he'd encouraged me throughout the previous day. When I pulled myself out of bed, I had a renewed sense of determination. *You can do this, Coyote,* I told myself, *because you're learning from the best.*

———

The sun was just as brutal as the day before. We hit the water just after breakfast, and the temperatures were beginning to climb. I'd learned from my mistakes and this time had brought along a dive mask, which would allow me to leap into the water with my eyes open. Aaron was skeptical. He worried that the mask might rip off my face when I hit the water, but I thought it was worth a shot. With the addition of the dive mask, along with an evening's reflection on what I had learned from Aaron, I felt a renewed sense of confidence that I would make a catch, as long as my eye was on the prize. As I recalled Aaron's instructions, I pictured the proper way to arc my body, the target moving through the water, and the speed of the boat. I understood how to time my dive to get slightly ahead of the turtle. I could do this, and nothing was going to stop me, right?

Nope. One slight issue stood in the way: There were no

turtles to be seen. For hours, the boat traveled up and down through every inch of water, and we spotted absolutely nothing. *Not one single turtle.*

"Let's call it a day, guys," Eddie said after lunch. "This is useless. The turtles must have moved somewhere else. Some days you catch 'em; some days you don't."

Mark, Mario, and I looked at one another with a silent, frustrated resignation. Even though we hadn't found any turtles on day two, we did get some great footage the day before and would still find a way to piece together a *decent* episode. Reluctantly, I accepted that, it was time to head back. I was disappointed, but to be honest, I felt a sense of relief. The jet lag was still taking a heavy toll on my mental and physical well-being. My legs felt wobbly under me, and my thoughts seemed to be one step behind my movements. As we set off, Eddie told us he was going to backtrack through an area that was somewhere between two and a half and five feet in depth.

"Sounds good, Eddie," I said. "Thank you for everything."

Eddie navigated the boat around some rocks and headed into a channel. Aaron had taught me to never stop looking, so he and I stood at the front of the boat like we had all day. Still staring down, still hoping to see a shadow. Suddenly, as the boat puttered slowly back toward land, we looked down and noticed a dark, round object shifting in and out of view like a phantom between the waves and the shadows.

Oh my gosh, I thought, *is that what I think it is, or am I dreaming?*

Chapter 4 / Diving for Sea Turtles!

"It's a turtle," Aaron said. "You've got this, Coyote."

Under threat from a predator, a green sea turtle often employs an interesting escape strategy: swimming toward another turtle in order to distract whatever's chasing them. Their thinking seems to be that that the predator will decide they're not worth following and instead attack the other turtle, giving the original turtle a short window of time to swim away. That was the case here because this small reptile led us right to another turtle—and it was *huge*! The larger specimen immediately exploded into action and the chase was on. Coyote Peterson had one last chance to catch a sea turtle!

"Dive when it comes up for air," Aaron said, "because when the turtle breaches is when it slows down."

I waited, and the large turtle moved right, then left, with Eddie keeping pace right along with it. Through all the zigs and zags, I held on for dear life, and then, as predicted, I saw the turtle slow down ever so slightly and tracked it as it surged toward the surface. Waiting for Aaron's command, I gathered my confidence.

This is my moment, I thought. *It's turtle time.*

"Go for it," Aaron said.

I adjusted my mask, raised my arms, and jumped. Immediately, I felt a rush of adrenaline speed through my tired limbs. Time seemed to slow down as I entered the water hands first, my head following as I plunged forward. My legs encountered resistance, and I knew immediately I'd landed just ahead of the turtle—right where I wanted to be!

I didn't realize it at the time, but after running the scene through my head repeatedly, talking to Aaron, and reviewing my GoPro footage from the day before, I now know that when I hit the water, I caused a small current that displaced the turtle. This current pushed the reptile down just enough to throw it off its rhythm, giving me a chance to make a catch. In the moment, though, all I could comprehend was that I'd landed just to the side of the turtle, and the immense pressure to not lose this one. So I ran my fingers down the top of its body, and almost instinctually, I slipped my fingers under the rear rim of its shell and held on as it thrust forward. Feeling a hesitation in the turtle's movement, I shimmied my body up the length of the shell toward its head and pulled back. The turtle lunged as I directed its momentum upward, and we saw the light of the sun as we rose to the surface together.

Whoosh. The turtle and I breached, and I steadied myself, adjusting my grip to ensure it couldn't slip away.

Aaron and Mark had jumped from the boat while I was underwater, and they swam right up to me, huge smiles on their faces. Everyone was ecstatic.

"That is a good-size turtle right there!" I screamed, amazed by how the combination of luck, determination, and training had ultimately led me to successfully executing an amazing catch. "Without question, that is the biggest turtle I have ever caught!"

We carefully swam with it back to the boat, and before we hauled the behemoth up to be measured and weighed, we identified that this turtle was a male—the second one we'd encountered in two days. Finding big, healthy males in the ocean is a great sign because it means the turtle population will have a chance to improve, paving the way for larger, more robust turtles for generations to come. We also noticed that he was untagged, which is extremely special because this turtle would provide brand-new data for the Gudjuda Rangers. As I sat on the boat with this spectacular creature, I marveled at the magnitude of his presence.

"Look at the size of this turtle's tail!" I said to the camera. "Just like a snapping turtle's, male green sea turtles have extremely long tails, as long and as big around as my arm. That is an absolute dragon tail right there!"

Then I looked into the turtle's eyes, which were fixed ahead as he swished his flippers back and forth.

"Now, you may notice that the turtle's eyes are very wet," I said, holding up his head. "He almost looks like he's crying. He's *not* crying. All turtles are capable of secreting a mucus from their eye membrane to keep their eyes wet when they're out of the water. This goes for all turtles."

Then I pointed out his beak, noting how round it was because, unlike

98

a snapping turtle, a sea turtle doesn't use its beak to hunt and kill prey.

"When they get to be this big, they're completely herbivores," I said. "They just sift along the bottom of the ocean, eating algae and sea grass. And if you look at the underside…the lower part of the jaw is serrated, and they have bolt-cutter-like power. They could easily snip off one of your fingers!"

Boy, did Mario know that well! I thought off camera. *One almost ripped the arm off his wet suit!*

After admiring the turtle and presenting a few pertinent facts for the camera, it was time to collect his biometric data. We gently slid the heavy reptile into a harness and hoisted him up with a crank scale to measure his weight. At two hundred thirty

pounds, he clocked in as one of the ten biggest turtles ever recorded by the Rangers! As we lowered him back down, he

moved his flippers back and forth, as if he were signaling to us that he was ready to swim home. It was time for us to return this giant to the ocean but before we let him go, we had to tag him. Holding the turtle's left flipper in my hands, I moved the tagging device between two of his large, leathery scales and clamped down. Quick and painless—the big guy was successfully tagged!

I turned and looked at the group. "I name all the turtles I catch, and I think we're going to call this one Eddie."

Chapter 4 / Diving for Sea Turtles!

It's a fitting name for a true legend of the sea, and a moment of honor for the brave captain who had navigated our course of adventure over the last two days. As Aaron and I released the turtle back into the sea, I thought about how I would never forget this turtle, the challenge he was to catch, or my time spent working alongside the Gudjuda Rangers. Every student needs a good teacher for guidance on their journey of following their dreams, and I'm honored that Aaron bestowed his invaluable skills and profound knowledge upon me. He showed me not only the best way to respect these spectacular reptiles, but he also demonstrated the peaceful unity that exists between the sea turtles and the Rangers tasked with protecting them and their natural habitat. Together, humans and turtles have enjoyed these waters for thousands of years, and for a few unspoiled hours, I was able to sit at their table in harmony. To catch, admire, and share with our audience the splendor of the green sea turtle was a life goal that became a dream come true.

Chapter Five
King of the Savanna!

Chapter 5 / King of the Savanna!

I f you're like most people, you probably spend your days running around from one task to the next. You're juggling classes, homework, sports practice, yearbook meetings, music lessons, and family obligations, all while incessantly checking your texts and social media in order to keep up with your best friends. We're all so busy these days, and our attention is constantly pulled in a hundred different directions. We rarely allow ourselves to stop and be in the moment. I feel extremely lucky to have a job that allows me to venture out into the wilderness and experience the natural world, but I often feel rushed to catch the most impressive animal, capture *the* perfect shot, or conquer the kinds of feats no other animal adventurer has before. Nowadays, chasing your dreams comes with a lot of pressure!

All that being said, when I traveled to South Africa in early 2018 to tranquilize and collect the biometric data from a pride of lions, I learned an important life lesson: In the midst of making your biggest, wildest goals a reality, you will find the greatest satisfaction and fulfillment when you allow yourself to be present. Sometimes you need to stop...and smell a lion.

Hang on for a second. Stop and smell a lion?! Isn't it "stop and smell the roses?" Okay, okay, I know that's what you're thinking, but read on and allow me to explain....

———————

It was a bright-blue morning. The air was dry and crisp. The rays of sun streamed down from the sky, warming the

ground as Mario, Mark, and I woke up on the Kariega Game
Reserve, one of the most renowned wildlife sanctuaries in
South Africa. At twenty-five thousand acres, this pristine,
private expanse is home to many native species including lions,
elephants, ostriches, rhinoceros, giraffes, leopards, buffalo,
hippopotamuses, antelopes, wildebeest, and countless birds and
reptiles. A sort of Jurassic Park without the dinosaurs, these
animals freely roam up its dry, dusty hills, venture out across its
rolling, scrub-covered savanna grasslands, or seek shelter in its
dense acacia woodlands, protected from poachers and human
encroachment by a surrounding perimeter fence. Tourists
flock to Kariega to stay in one of its many luxury lodges and
experience guided safaris to capture photographs of the stunning
wildlife. But the Brave Wilderness crew had something much
more special in mind for our expedition. We didn't want to go
out on safari and sit idly in a vehicle, a set of binoculars glued to
our eyeballs. Instead, we flew to Kariega determined to track
lions, the kings of the savanna, like old-time explorers. Our
hope was to encounter a pride of lions purely and naturally
before attempting to get our cameras up close.

Kariega is divided into two distinct areas by a gated fence.
On one side live the megafauna, namely lions and larger
mammals such as the elephants and giraffes. On the other side
live the smaller, hoofed mammals like zebras and impalas.
Periodically, these more vulnerable animals, or prey, are released
to the predator side, where they're hunted and eaten. This
carefully monitored system allows the habitat to maintain a

Chapter 5 / King of the Savanna!

healthy, natural balance, with no predator wiping out entire herds of wildebeest or antelope and no single species becoming overpopulated.

———

Before Mark, Mario, and I embarked upon this adventure, we'd made contact with a man named LB Williams, who you may remember from earlier in the book when he took us on our spectacular tide-pool adventure. LB had collaborated on several conservation projects with the rangers and veterinarians at Kariega in the past, and was confident that they could help us on our quest to get hands-on with a pride of lions, providing a unique animal encounter with Africa's most famous predator.

"They've had an incredibly healthy, stable pride of lions on the reserve since 2004," he told us. "I promise that if you want to have an unforgettable encounter with the most beautiful lions in South Africa, that's your spot."

While I'd never been particularly obsessed with lions growing up, I'd always respected them. They are top predators, after all, and if I wanted to make my dream of encountering the world's most impressive animals come true, the African lion—the most revered mammalian species in South Africa—was definitely on my list. With their massive muscular bodies, thick manes, gargantuan paws with sharp claws, and gleaming rows of flesh-ripping teeth, lions have always been symbols of courage, strength, and ferocity. Because they're found so often in zoos, circuses, and movies, people take them for granted. These spectacular cats used to roam throughout Africa and into parts of Asia and Europe, but now their range is limited to parts of sub-Saharan Africa. Poaching, trophy hunting, and human encroachment have caused their numbers to plummet, and while at one point in time there were as many as four hundred fifty thousand lions in Africa, today there are only twenty to thirty thousand. In fact, it's estimated that half Africa's remaining lions may be lost by 2035. The Brave Wilderness crew hoped to reverse that terrible trend by bringing attention to the African lion's remarkable beauty and uniqueness, impressing upon the world that these are creatures to be cared for, respected, and preserved—not destroyed.

Just after dawn, Mark, Mario, and I met up with our field guide, Jo Haesslich, and a team of field veterinarians, including Dr. Waldo Dreyer, who'd be responsible for tranquilizing the lions before we could approach them and collect vital data. Our plan was to pile into an open-top Land Cruiser with Jo and head in one direction, while the veterinarians drove to another part of the reserve, each of us tracking the pride. To be honest, we had no idea what—if anything—we'd find. Kariega's pride doesn't wear radio transmitters or tracking devices, and the lions can move miles overnight, hiding in the shadows of trees or in underbrush, to avoid the heat of the scorching sun.

"We're going to have to look for signs of the lions in order to locate them," said Jo, "so keep your eyes peeled for tracks, scat, or a fresh kill."

I felt like a true explorer out of a history book! And today we were going to use the same techniques that people used to track apex predators hundreds of years ago!

While lions typically aren't aggressive against humans unless they're provoked, we traveled within the safety of our vehicle, so that we could cover a more extensive stretch of terrain. The vehicle lent us a solid barrier and protection, as lions tend to shy away from large, mobile, man-made objects. To the lions, the Land Cruiser is a comparatively larger threat, making us seem more powerful than we are. They react to elephants the same way, something we would eventually witness while on the Kariega Game Reserve.

For hours, Jo drove us up brush-covered hills, down dusty roads, and through the vast open wilderness of the savanna looking for signs of the pride. At different points, we would stop and I would venture out on foot to look for environmental indicators. One of the coolest signs we found was the skull of a wildebeest, snapped off at the point where its head would have met its neck. Unfortunately for us, the skull was old, and there were no lions in sight. Mario also found a zebra's leg bone, still covered in bristly fur and a few scraps of leathery flesh, and spotted a pile of days-old dried-up scat. But still...no lions. My heart began to fall in my chest. *Would we ever find the pride?*

Yes, we would! Because just minutes later, as our Land Cruiser bumped down a dirt road and almost bottomed out in a deep, muddy puddle along a stream, we noticed a fresh paw print in the mud! Tracks are the most reliable signs of lion activity, so the pride was likely close! I jumped out of the vehicle to take a closer look.

"Check this out, guys," I said to the camera while placing my hand next to the muddy impression for scale. "Completely fresh lion track, right there. Like most cats, lions try to avoid walking in the water, so the cat definitely moved around the puddle and up the road here. That means we are hot on the pride's trail."

But I had no idea just *how* hot we were. While I carefully inspected the print and the area around it a little more, the Land Cruiser's radio crackled to life. A broken-up voice came over the

airwaves, and Jo listened closely, then turned to Mark.

"There are literally lions on the top of this hill," she said, pointing just off in the distance to her left.

"So the other team's got eyes on the lions?" Mark asked.

"Yeah, yeah," Jo said and smiled. "And they're on a kill!"

Mark sprang into action and immediately called out to me. I was still nearby and quickly responded. When he told me the news, I grabbed Mario, and we sprinted toward the Land Cruiser, then leaped in as Jo started up the engine.

This was it! It was finally time to encounter a pride of lions!

Based on the other team's location, the lions weren't that far away, but that was as the crow flies. Getting there in our Land Cruiser required driving back over the same unpaved roads we'd headed down earlier, winding our way down, then up, as a cloud of dust plumed up in the wake of our vehicle. After about fifteen minutes, we finally reunited with the other half of our team and I was eager to see the pride. I was nearly jumping out of my skin. Before we got to the clearing where the pride was having their feast, though, we met up with Dr. Dreyer so he could climb into our vehicle with the tranquilizer gun. It was an impressive tool.

That looks like a sniper rifle you'd find in the military, I thought. Then he presented us with the tranquilizer darts. They actually bore a very similar resemblance to the darts you might throw in your best friend's basement on a Friday night. They were close to six inches in length, cylindrical, spring-loaded for serum injection, and capped with razor-sharp, heavy gauge tips!

"Is this going to hurt the lions?" I asked.

"Absolutely not," Dr. Dreyer replied. "This feels like a bee sting to them."

If there's anything Coyote Peterson knows intimately, it's getting stung, so this news came as a huge relief. Dr. Dreyer then explained that the tranquilizer gun was powered by carbon dioxide cylinders that launch the darts through the air with incredible speed and accuracy—but with next to no sound when shot. The most important consideration was aim; Dr. Dreyer would need to shoot the lions in parts of their bodies that were thick with muscle mass, like their front shoulders or hindquarters.

As small, patchy clouds moved across the sky and a low hum of insects rang steadily in my ears, we rolled up slowly and carefully to the top of a hill, eyeing a grassy clearing that was off to our right. With binoculars up to my eyes, I spotted him about a hundred yards in the distance: He was the most formidable and awe-inspiring animal specimen I'd seen on any one of my many epic animal adventures. Crouched low to the ground behind a small bush, with his paws in front of him and his majestic, yellow-maned head lifted, was the one and only king of the savanna!

There were actually four lions in total, one male and three females. The male stood watch as the females paced back and forth around the fallen carcass of an impala, a fresh kill that was little more than a late-morning snack to these monstrous cats. I knew this wasn't the full pride because a pride typically consists of around three males, a dozen or so females, and a collection of their young. As in any pride, these three females were likely related, and they'd worked as a team to track the impala and ambush it. Lions are carnivores, and the females hunt hoofed mammals like wildebeest, antelope, zebras, or impalas within a territory that's approximately one hundred square miles.

Dr. Dreyer explained that, based on his size, the male lion wasn't quite a full-grown adult; he was considered a subadult, so he certainly wasn't the head of the pride. That title belonged to a Mufasa-like beast with a full, dark-brown mane, who hadn't been spotted in days. To me, however, this lion's stature made no difference. As far as I was concerned, he was incredible! I knew that the young lion before me was lucky to live where he did—safe in the fenced-in confines of the Kariega Game Reserve—because most male lions have only a one-in-eight chance of surviving into adulthood. When male cubs reach sexual maturity at the age of two, they're kicked out of the pride by the other males, and they wander into the open savanna—either alone or with their brothers and cousins—searching for a new pride. Along the way, they hunt large prey like buffalo and giraffes, but they often succumb to harsh conditions or are eliminated by poachers or hunters. If they survive the trials of the savanna, they must find and take over another pride. Often these battles with strong resident lions can end in severe injury and even death.

Two of the three females hunkered down over the impala while the male lion paced around cautiously examining the approaching caravan of human observers. Eventually, the male settled and turned his attention to the carcass. The shift in feeding structure forced one of the females to turn her hindquarters in the direction of Dr. Dreyer's tranquilizer gun. The veterinarian carefully loaded a dart into the firing chamber, lifted the barrel, peered down the scope and pulled the trigger.

Roar! The female lion jumped up in the air like a kitten, the dart firmly lodged in her rump.

"*Oooh!*" I whispered. "Got one, got one. Nice shot."

The lions scampered behind the bushes, clearly startled. Moments later, and after a careful survey of their uninvited guests, they crept back to their impala snack, seemingly unperturbed by the sudden interruption. The male remained vigilant and kept his cover until hunger got the best of him. Another female, hesitant to join her companions, stood back, her long body poised right in our sight line. Her stance presented the perfect target, and Dr. Dreyer shot again. *Pow!* Success! He hit her directly in the front right leg.

My heart was pounding in my chest as sweat trickled down my forehead. Dr. Dreyer was one of the finest sharpshooters I'd ever seen, but the suspense was nearly too much to handle. Every time he raised the gun, I worried that the remaining lions would flee. Then we would be left in the precarious position of having untranquilized lions lurking in the underbrush while we collected data. Believe me, the last thing you want is to be looking over your shoulder, worrying about being stalked by a lion!

But Dr. Dreyer was an expert. The male lion scanned the area, seeking the faintest scent of a threat, and as he paced back and forth, Dr. Dreyer took aim. He pulled the trigger, darting him squarely in the right front leg. One lioness still hadn't been darted, so we carefully moved the vehicle to her.

It wasn't difficult. The fourth lion was just a few yards away, concealed under a scrubby bush. The Land Cruiser inched forward, past the darted lions, who were starting to look drowsy, and rolled to a stop. For this last and final shot, Dr. Dreyer raised his gun, and I held my breath. *One, two, three… He got her!* Four darts, four lions. And now it was time to get up close!

"Not yet," Dr. Dreyer said. "They might look like they're almost sedated, but you've really got to let that serum set in."

For several minutes, we waited in heated anticipation until Dr. Dreyer exited the Land Cruiser. He cautiously started walking toward the male lion, then stopped, bent down, and picked up a few small rocks. With a calm precision, he tossed them one by one near the subdued cat. The beast did not stir. Dr. Dreyer crept closer and with an outstretched hand, he gently lifted the lion's tail to confirm that the lion was fully sedated. The lion startled and lurched forward, causing Dr. Dreyer to instantly jump back! After a few minutes (and a few extra rocks thrown), confident that the lions were finally unconscious, he signaled that is was safe to approach. The last female shot was still collapsed under the bush, so some of the veterinary crew had to crouch down, climb in, and drag her out. Weighing in at about two hundred seventy-five pounds, the lioness was manageable for two strong people.

While my primary interest was the male lion, the field vets had to tranquilize all the lions not only for the team's safety, but because collecting biometric data on both males and females was necessary for their ongoing research. So while I headed straight to the big male, they walked over to the females. Together, they measured each of their bodies head to rump, checked the length of their tails, and measured the height and width of each of their

paws. Then they pulled fur samples from the tufts of their tails, checked their claws, and took a small sample of blood from each to determine if they were pregnant. Finally, they scanned the internal ID tags on each of the lions. One of the main goals of the Kariega Game Reserve is to have all their lions tagged. This helps identify each individual animal and streamlines the collection of data, allowing the health of the lion to be monitored whenever they're darted, which typically happens every few years.

"You've got about twenty minutes to film before he starts to wake up, Coyote," Dr. Dreyer said. "So, enjoy yourself…and be careful."

Unlike snapping turtles and wolverines, I'd never been fixated on lions, though I always thought they were impressive. Crouching behind this tranquilized king of the savanna that day, though, I was awestruck and any indifference was replaced by reverence. I'm telling you, Coyote Pack: You cannot truly appreciate the size and magnificence of a lion until you're actually next to one. Stretched out on the ground before me, this incredible beast was almost the size of a horse—not in height, but in length and mass.

"This creature is enormous, and it is still a subadult male lion," I said. I moved in front of the sleeping predator and lifted up his foreleg. "Look at the size of this animal's paw! It is bigger than my hand! That is crazy! It is so heavy, too. So much weight and so much muscle." Then I paused. "But you guys want to see those claws, don't you?"

"Oh yeah," Mark answered on behalf of all the viewers.

I pushed on either side of the lion's paw so that his claws would extend out, and I couldn't believe my eyes. They were curved like grappling hooks, as thick as my fingers, and almost two inches long, ending in needle-sharp tips! "These claws are constantly growing throughout the course of this animal's life. And, like all cats, it has four toes up front and a dewclaw on its side. That dewclaw is a key piece of predatory artillery because when they lunge toward a water buffalo or a wildebeest, and they latch on, it's this claw that hooks in place so that their prey cannot get away. That's what they do. They latch on and go for the neck."

We didn't weigh the big cat, but one of the vets estimated he weighed about 400 pounds, which was huge, considering that most adult males weigh anywhere from 265 to 420 pounds. So when this lion reached full-adult status, he would be a big boy, certainly capable of one day ruling his own pride! I ran my hand down the length of the lion's body and I couldn't believe the density of the muscle. If an apex predator like this were to attack a human, there was little chance you would be able to effectively fight back. They are so big, so fast, and so strong that overtaking a full-grown human would be swift and potentially lethal.

I rubbed his big, soft ears between my hands, and then I ran my fingers through his thick, straw-colored mane, which I knew would likely grow darker as he matured. The hair was courser than I expected, like a horse's mane rather than a housecat's plush coat. Then I lowered my face to the lion's body and did something I'd never considered doing. I paused, breathed in, and smelled the lion....

You might think I'm crazy, but in the moment, it seemed like the most natural thing to do, and truth be told...I was curious. I mean, when else are you ever going to be able to smell a lion? So, what does it smell like? Well, a lion smells absolutely divine—like a mixture of dry grassland, with a hint of sand and just a dash of old library book—and you can trust me when I say that there is absolutely nothing stinky about this creature. With a nose full of lion scent, I knew in an instant that I had reached the summit of something great; Coyote Peterson and the king of the savanna existed side by side in one harmonious moment.

A cloth was covering the lion's face, and I pulled it off, revealing his gently downturned mouth, dense whiskers, and soft nose. Then I peeled back his lips, revealing what I knew the Coyote Pack would be waiting for…the lion's flesh-ripping teeth!

"Look at those canines!" I said in genuine shock because they were *huge*. Measuring nearly ten centimeters in length, the lion's canines shot down from his gums like spears. I've seen the teeth of crocodiles and grizzly bears, and you can believe me when I say that they are mild when compared to these lethal weapons.

"Lions have three types of teeth," I continued. "Up front, you have these incisors, which are used to carry things like cubs and to pull meat away from the bones. The canines are used to inflict a kill, and then in the back here are the premolars, which are used like serrated shears to saw through the meat."

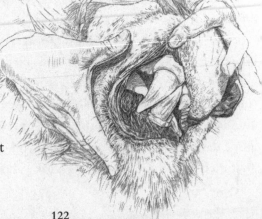

Then I looked at his tongue, and I was just as amazed by it as I was with his teeth.

"It's incredibly grippy," I said, "like sandpaper. They can actually use this tongue to lick meat away from bones. They can lick fur off, and believe it or not, if a lion were to lick your skin, it would take it right off! Not exactly like your housecat." Lions also use their powerful tongues to groom their bodies, which explains why he was so clean.

I then stepped back and let Dr. Dreyer collect the lion's biometric data and check for his ID tag. He pulled out a flexible measuring tape, recorded his length and paw size, noted some of the unique markings on his face, and then stopped and smiled.

"This male lion hasn't been tagged," he said, "so it's a good thing we got him today."

This was amazing! After a small microchip about the size of a grain of rice was embedded in the skin of his neck, this marvelous apex predator would help provide a brand-new set of data for the scientists to use when determining the health of the pride.

In one last moment of connection between me and the lion, I rested my face upon its sleeping head, thanking this beautiful animal in my mind for such an unbelievable experience. The truth is that the entire day was one gratifying, life-affirming moment followed by another. Yet the best was still to come because several hours after we finished collecting data and the lions had woken up from the procedure, we piled back into Jo's Land Cruiser and went on a sunset drive. We returned to the same area where we'd seen the pride, just to investigate whether they lingered or had already moved on. Jo brought the vehicle

Chapter 5 / King of the Savanna!

to a halt and as we sat in still silence, listening to the sounds of the oncoming night. Suddenly, a thundering roar echoed from some nearby trees and, almost as if manifested from nothing, the silhouette of a lion appeared in the stark rays of setting sunlight. With cameras rolling, we watched as the male lion we'd spent such precious time with stepped into our path, lifted his eyes to the setting sun, paused, and roared once more. In that moment, I realized I felt more present and in tune with lions than any other predatory mammal I'd ever had a chance to interact with. I've had unforgettable encounters with grizzly bears, badgers, and foxes over my tenure as a wildlife expert. I've even gone hand-to-paw with one of the world's most elusive and ferocious predators, the wolverine. But getting the chance to be in the presence of lions in a tranquil form was a humbling honor that, even in my wildest dreams, I never imagined possible. There is a beauty in these predatory beasts that is unlike anything I have ever witnessed, and my encounter with the king of the savanna was one I will remember for the rest of my life.

If you're working hard to set goals and build upon them, take a deep breath, be present, and enjoy a beautiful moment or interaction authentically. I promise you that calm solitude and reflection will reignite your drive, enliven your senses, and give you the mental clarity to go out and pursue your dreams.

Chapter Six
Slimed by a Salamander!

Chapter 6 / Slimed by a Salamander!

I t's been said that all good things come to those who wait. While that's often the case, I think you need to be more specific to capture the *true* essence of that saying. In my experience, some of life's most exciting adventures—the ones that have helped me actualize my wildest, most-wished-for dreams—have happened because I was patient, dedicated, and persistent. At the early age of eight, I never would have caught the giant snapping turtle I'd nicknamed "the Dragon" if I hadn't first tried dozens of times, falling butt-first into the mud and ruining half my socks. I never would have landed a migrating sockeye salmon in a freezing-cold lake in Alaska if I hadn't forced myself to paddle for hours, searching through harsh environmental conditions. And I never would have planted myself on the back of a green sea turtle in the warm, clear expanse of the Coral Sea if I hadn't practiced for two straight days—missing my target again and again! On all these epic adventures, I watched, I waited, I learned, and in some cases struggled relentlessly...but finally, I did it! When you chase your dreams, I think you've got do the same: Be patient and tireless, even when it seems like achieving the goal is impossible. Trust me, you'll get there, you just have to work for it!

In spring of 2017, the Brave Wilderness team and I traveled into the hollows of West Virginia to search for the largest and rarest salamander species in North America: the elusive hellbender. This amphibian is so creepy and ominous-looking that early American settlers believed they might be demonic creatures who'd clawed their way up from the pits of hell; hence their name. In reality, hellbenders are one of the most harmless, fragile species on the planet. Due to their reclusive nature and a tendency for sheltering under rocks in remote, fast-moving streams—where they often stay for weeks—they're also among the most difficult amphibians to find.

Many of you know that I've been catching salamanders since I was a kid. My rural neighborhood in Newbury, Ohio, was near several small streams and ponds, and my friends and I liked nothing more than to explore them after school and on the weekends. Getting our shoes wet and our hands dirty, we'd turn over the flat, moss-covered rocks that sat near the edge of the water, and we'd cheer with delight when we uncovered the black racing stripes of a northern two-lined salamander or the unmistakable bright-yellow dots on the back of a spotted salamander. I'll never forget my first dusky salamander, a spotty, brownish amphibian with a white belly, who I found crouched under a pile of wet leaves. These salamanders were small but special, and when I carefully scooped up their slimy, delicate bodies and placed them in the palms of my hands, I felt as if I'd uncovered a long-lost buried treasure. But for a curious, intrepid young explorer like me, catching these creatures was way too easy. They were practically in my backyard, they were always near water, and all I had to do was roll over a log, rummage through some leaves, or lift up a wet slab of stone to find them. A challenging adventure this was *not*—and that's why I always dreamed of finding the hidden, misunderstood amphibian known as the *Cryptobranchus alleganiensis*, or more commonly, the Eastern hellbender.

Greenish brown, splotchy, and sometimes lightly spotted with black or orange flecks, hellbenders are incredibly well camouflaged. Those who have been fortunate enough to see one in the wild are baffled by its bizarre appearance. Perhaps the struggle to identify this unique creature is what resulted in a long list of nicknames; they may actually have more nicknames than any amphibian species in the world. A few of the most popular tags include: "lasagna lizards," "devil dogs," "mud-devils," "water dogs," and even "Alleghany alligators." When it comes to the shape of their bodies, hellbenders are long and flat, with small, beady eyes and skin so slippery that handling them feels like you just sneezed up the contents of your stuffy nose into your hands. Yes, they feel that gross! Personally, my favorite nickname is the "snot otter." If you ever happen to see one swimming, they do have a style of motion that is very similar to this mammalian predator. Combine that with their brown coloration, long bodies, and a thick layer of slime, and you can see where "snot otter" originates from.

When we dreamed up the idea of finding and filming a hellbender in the wild, Mario reconnected with his longtime friend and colleague Tim Brust, a field herpetologist who catches, records, and releases reptile and amphibian species throughout Appalachia. Tim is frequently hired by developers or manufacturers concerned about the environmental impact their construction or business might have on the natural environment, and his work cataloging and studying the effects of pollution on various native species has gone a long way in ensuring the survival of animals like the hellbender.

Preserving and protecting these animals is important in and of itself but is also beneficial to monitoring the health of the environment. This is because in many regions, salamanders are considered an "indicator species," meaning that if they're abundant and healthy, their environment will be rich and healthy, too. Hellbenders absorb a great deal of their environment through their skin. So when pollutants like pesticides from farm runoff or toxic construction waste enter the water system, and ultimately their bodies, it builds up over time and can eventually cause fatalities. Larvae and young hellbenders are even more susceptible to these toxins because—unlike older salamanders—they haven't developed immunities or a resistance to environmental impurities. Unlike a large dose of toxic chemicals released all at once, the slow and continuous seep of pollution by human industry accumulates steadily, spreading throughout delicate ecosystems, contaminating the soil and water systems. Human encroachment has wiped out several reproducing populations of hellbenders—which is why they're now classified as a near-threatened species.

The part of northeastern West Virginia we were heading to is protected for conservation purposes, so I can't tell you exactly where we met Tim. But I can say that it was near the town of Elkins, deep in the heart of the Appalachian Mountains. This location stands out as one of the most beautiful places we have ever filmed. With its gently flowing streams, hidden valleys, and expansive green meadows, this was wild and wonderful West Virginia at its finest. When we arrived in early May, the fields of bluebells

and columbines were in full bloom, and migrating warblers and thrushes had returned to their nests, where they'd keep watch over their soon-to-hatch eggs. The temperature was in the mid-seventies, and the bright morning sun was warm on our backs when we met Tim for the start of our hellbender adventure, but he warned us not to get too comfortable.

"The stream we'll be searching in is ice cold," he said in his West Virginian drawl, "so we're all going to have to wear wet suits."

Most of us picture reptiles and amphibians as being creatures who spend their lives searching for warmth. Whether in a sweltering rain forest, a dry desert, or happily perched and basking in the sun on rocks near the edges of lakes. That's the exact *opposite* of what hellbenders do. Much like Chinese and Japanese giant salamanders—the only two larger salamanders than the species we were looking for—hellbenders spend the entirety of their lives underwater in frigid mountain streams, like the one I found myself approaching on that spring morning. This shallow creek twisted its way down the hills and into a lush green valley, where its gentle rapids and swift current flowed over large, flat, and sometimes slippery rocks just below the surface. The water was only about three feet at its deepest points, but it stayed cold throughout, no matter how hard the sun was shining on it. Yet Mark, Mario, Tim, and I were planning to float face first in it for hours, looking under every one of its flat rocks for a hellbender!

Unlike the method I used when I used to search for salamanders as a kid, we weren't going to be turning over any rocks to find hellbenders. If we did, not only would we agitating the dirt of the riverbed, distorting our view while searching, but we'd also be disrupting the habitat of any creatures who called these crevices home. Hellbenders are very territorial, and if their secluded, watery dens are exposed, there's a good chance they will move somewhere else. That's why our plan was to move as few rocks as possible while slowly working upstream, so that the silt we did disturb would flow down in the opposite direction, right past the places we'd already searched.

Even though it was morning, the sun was already so high and bright in the sky that it was shooting glorious, radiant sunbeams into the stream, illuminating the icy current and giving us a very clear look at the underwater world before us. The light cut shadows through the trees and onto the banks, creating a few shady spots where we could set up base camp. We found a nice, flat area, unloaded our gear, and then washed our hands so they'd be free of any bug spray, sunscreen, or hand lotion that the salamanders might absorb into their skin. We put on our wet suits, and I exchanged my cowboy hat for a dive mask. Fully suited, I walked toward the stream right behind Tim and stepped in. I pulled my mask over my eyes, knelt down, and placed my face just beneath the surface. The water

was absolutely freezing and sent a chill down my spine that took my breath away, challenging my determination. It felt like an ice bath!

How am I going to float in this for ten minutes? I asked myself. *Much less the two or three hours Tim says it might take to find a hellbender?*

Apparently, though, Tim didn't even seem to notice the cold. When I looked up toward him, he was already belly-down in the water, working his way up the stream while he reached his hands carefully under the edges of the rocks, then dove down to peer under them.

"Well, this certainly isn't going to be like snorkeling in the Bahamas," Mark said to me, smiling.

The good thing about wearing a wet suit is that as soon as it's completely saturated, your natural body heat warms the water trapped inside. So once I was fully submerged and started to move, the initial state of being "frozen" began to dissipate. I stayed low and followed Tim's lead, wandering upstream from flat rock to flat rock, dunking my head beneath the water to inspect each and every one, hoping to spot a hellbender. The water was generally clear, but the strong flow still brought with it enough sediment to reduce my vision. So as a secondary means of investigation, I would feel with my fingers beneath the rim of each slab, checking for anything slimy that I might have missed visually. At first the heated anticipation of the search kept us all mentally focused and the freezing temperatures tolerable. But as the hours passed by and our efforts were proving fruitless, the cold began to take its toll.

"This is as cold as I felt when we went to Alaska to catch sockeye salmon!" I yelled to Mario. But he didn't answer. His teeth were chattering so hard that it was impossible for him to form coherent words.

We'd been searching under every rock imaginable, yet there wasn't a single hellbender to be found, and I was worried that the team was showing early signs of hypothermia. The sun had now reached its highest point in the sky, and it was time to take advantage of its warmth. "I've got to get out and warm up!" I yelled to Tim. He looked up and nodded, then took his mask off and walked over to join me on the stream's banks. Our lips were purple, our fingers wrinkled and white, and our skin was numb from decreased circulation. For about thirty minutes, we did all we could to warm up, including jumping-jack and push-up contests to get our blood flowing more rapidly. I looked at Tim, seeing an expression of frustration on his face, as he pondered the time and distance we had traveled and searched with no slimy results. We exchanged glances, and without a word, we agreed it was time to get back into the water. We gathered our courage and set off, wading out into the stream, determined to find the elusive hellbender.

Patience is the key, I said to myself, *because sometimes the best adventures in life come your way only when you don't give up.*

I crouched down, took a deep breath, and stuck my face back into the water. An hour passed, then another, yet still, there wasn't a single hellbender to be found. My body temperature

was continuing to drop, and it seemed as if this adventure was going to result in defeat. I sat up in the flowing water and looked around me, trying to gain my bearings and the location of Mark, Mario, and Tim. Roughly twenty yards away, I could see that Tim was submerged and the cameras were directed down toward him. Mark noticed my gaze and motioned me over to a sunny spot on the opposite side of the river. When I got there, Tim was still flat on his belly, his whole head underwater as if his face were glued to the edge of a rock.

"Do you have one?" I asked, and Tim lifted his arm out of the water, giving us a thumbs-up.

"Hellbender's looking right at me in the face," he answered.

Holy mackerel! This was it, we'd finally found the elusive creature we'd been searching for! But just because you've found a hellbender, doesn't mean you have caught it. I knew it wasn't going to be all smooth sailing from here. Getting a hellbender out from under a rock is a difficult and incredibly delicate process that would require two people, one narrow stick, and a net. We couldn't just reach down under the rock and blindly grope for the animal; first off, it might retreat farther back into its burrow, but secondly, this giant salamander is so slippery that we'd never be able to get a firm grip on it, so a hand catch was out of the question. We planned to use a technique Tim called "tickling," in which we'd maneuver a long, skinny stick carefully into the crevice where the hellbender was hunkered down, position the tip of the stick just behind the amphibian and tickle its tail. Like many underwater animals, especially

139

ones with poor eyesight, when a hellbender feels something at its back, it doesn't turn around, like a human would. Instead, it assumes another creature has crept up behind it, and it darts forward to escape. If all went well and the hellbender responded as we predicted, I'd be waiting for it with a net, ready to scoop it up and carry the slippery salamander to shore so we could have a closer look and record its biometric data.

The only issue was (and it was a *big* issue): What if the salamander tucked deeper under the rock, preventing us from coaxing it out? This was going to be a very precise operation! A fraction of an inch could mean the difference between a successful catch and a complete miss!

With my heart pounding in my chest, my GoPro in one hand, and the net in the other, I crouched low in the frigid stream. My plan was to submerge both just as Tim started tickling, capturing some good underwater shots of the hellbender and anticipating its forward lunge in my direction. We hoped that the salamander wouldn't catch a ride in the fast-flowing current, but instead would dart upstream using its feet and long, powerful, rudder-like tail. But of course, that's not what was about to happen.

"All right, the hellbender is right near the entrance to this hole," I said to the camera. "We have a really good chance of actually catching it."

Tim remained underwater, breathing through his snorkel. He extended the stick into the crevice. I dipped my GoPro into the water, ready to capture the scene, while I lowered the net

next to it. The water was rushing around our legs, and as Tim tickled the back of the hellbender with the end of the stick, just as we feared, the salamander thrust its tail and exploded straight into the current. Oh no…had we lost our prized specimen? Not today, Coyote Pack! As the startled amphibian darted past me, Tim had the incredible wherewithal to grab the net from my hand. With lighting speed, he placed the net between his legs, and by some miracle managed to scoop up the hellbender before it had the chance to escape! *YES!* It was a brilliant and unexpected combination of luck and quick intuition that made this the most epic amphibian catch of my life!

"Oh man, Tim; that was amazing!" I screamed after I lifted my head from the water and realized what had happened. We were so lucky! One false move and the swift water would have swept up the hellbender, sending it straight downriver and far out of our reach. We hollered and hooted with excitement, exchanging high fives and a pure release of admiration for the animal nestled in the net before us.

"Look at the size of that giant salamander!" I said, awestruck, as I rubbed my hand underneath its slimy body while it sat in the net.

"That's a big one," Tim replied, and he was right. According to field guide statistics, we could immediately tell this salamander's size was well above average, bigger than we could have ever hoped for! Patience and persistence against the freezing odds had paid off, and now it was time to show off this magnificent creature to the world.

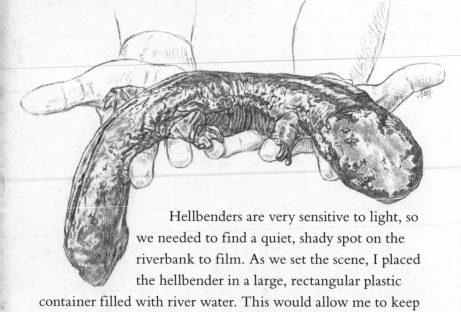

Hellbenders are very sensitive to light, so we needed to find a quiet, shady spot on the riverbank to film. As we set the scene, I placed the hellbender in a large, rectangular plastic container filled with river water. This would allow me to keep the fragile amphibian mostly submerged when presenting it. And while hellbenders definitely have lungs, they use them more for buoyancy than for oxygenation. So keeping the animal in fresh, cool water would also allow it to absorb much-needed oxygen through the fleshy, lateral skin flaps running along its sides.

I reached down and gently held the slimy hellbender in the palms of my hands, careful not to grip it too tightly. Because they're so delicate and slippery, these salamanders require great care to handle, so I was maneuvering my hands to allow the animal to naturally shift its position.

"You'll notice how flattened the shape of this amphibian's body is," I said, marveling at how its smooth, triangular head connected seamlessly to the long, speckled torso. "That is what allows them to easily slide underneath the crevices in between rocks, and then they work their bodies against the current as they're walking on the basin of a river looking for food."

Hellbenders hunt at night, and 90 percent of their diet is crayfish, though they also eat fish, smaller salamanders, and even other hellbenders. Downstream currents carry prey items past a waiting hellbender. Their small, glassy eyes aren't particularly acute, so they rely on chemicals and vibrations in the water to sense where and when another animal is present. With just the slightest scent or the feel of a tiny ripple on their slimy skin, they shoot a blast of water out of their mouths and—*shloop!*—suck up their meal! Using the tiny teeth on the upper and lower jaws of their mouths, they then crush their prey and—*GULP*—swallow it whole!

"One thing that I can feel that you guys can't quite see is that on the tips of their toes they have these little grippy pads," I said while Tim extended out the orange-tipped feet of the hellbender. "These help this amphibian grab on to the slimy rocks that are on the basin of the river."

The best way to visualize these pads is to think about how your own fingers feel after you've sat in the bath or pool for too long. They become wrinkled up and tight, with leathery ridges like the rain treads of a tire. Those small grippy toes pressed into my palm as I moved the hellbender and admired its striking colors, which Tim had assured me were some of the most magnificent he'd ever seen.

"Look at that coloration," I said, lowering its head out of frame and bringing its body into focus. "It's brown with slightly orange patterning. That allows it to stay perfectly camouflaged on the basin of the river."

I continued to present the characteristics of this wonderful creature to the audience, marveling at its unique structure. I couldn't believe I had this awesome amphibian in my hands!

"Look at that little face!" I said as its colors glinted in the light. "It's staying pretty calm, but I'm going to dip it back into the water. I need to make sure that this amphibian stays hydrated at all times." I lowered the salamander back into the tub, recalling its unique respiratory features. As though wanting to communicate, the alien-like creature responded and lifted its head, staring up at me.

"Well, hello," I said to it, almost about to laugh. "Hi there. What's your name? Should we name you? Herbie? Herbie the Hellbender?"

As if on cue, the hellbender lowered its head back into the water, releasing a quiet squeak, along with a few bubbles that burst on the surface.

"I think that's a yes," said Mark.

And now it was time to measure Herbie. Tim handed me a flexible tape measure, and I extended it from snout to tail along the amphibian's body. Most hellbenders range anywhere from nine and a half to sixteen inches, but Herbie was positively massive at a full twenty inches! I was astonished! If there was ever a doubt that we'd caught one of the most impressive hellbenders in all of West Virginia, this put it to rest.

"So, Coyote, how old is this amphibian?" Mark asked.

"Well, nobody really knows for sure how long they can live, but some scientists think they can live as long as thirty years in the wild and over fifty years in captivity. I would guess that this one, based on its size, is probably somewhere between twenty-five and thirty years of age."

Chapter 6 / Slimed by a Salamander!

In my opinion, that's a marvelously long life for such a delicate creature, especially considering that environmental pollutants can so easily wipe them out. This animal's size and age are further proof that this stretch of protected river wilderness in West Virginia is a healthy and thriving ecosystem. I would bet that after we placed Herbie the Hellbender back under his rock, we could return ten years later to find him flourishing in the same river!

I could have spent hours with this fascinating creature, but it was time for him to return to the wild. So Tim, Mario, Mark, and I carried this spectacular salamander back to his watery crevice. As we watched him disappear into the flowing water, I was confident he would continue to live out the wonderful life of a hellbender. I think we were all thankful for the health of this environment, and I was hopeful that this beautiful mountain stream would continue to be a safe haven for such a unique and interesting animal. It's fair to say that there is always more work in terms of conservation and regulation to be done, but Herbie's health was promising news for the hellbender population and is a testament to the successful protection of this species in the state of West Virginia.

A considerable amount of time has passed since my long, cold search for the hellbender, yet the importance of this animal in the grand scheme of our planet's health is always fresh in my mind. Being an indicator species, they fulfill one of the most important environmental functions in streams throughout Appalachia by reacting to changes in the ecosystem, which helps define the health of the environment. I hope that more people will recognize this importance and will support the protection of species like the hellbender. Without this larger salamander gauging the health of our rivers, the other smaller creatures within them stand the chance of being lost due to chemical imbalances. I'm honored to have met this misunderstood amphibian, who taught me that patience is a virtue; that hard, sometimes freezing work pays off; and that persistence will always be a key to making your dreams come true.

Chapter Seven
Surrounded by Killer Whales!

When you decide to pursue a big goal, you often feel a deep sense of hope and you want to dive right in, letting inspiration and passion guide you. When I made the choice to start an animal adventure channel on YouTube, I dreamed of huge, exciting things: meeting the world's most exotic animals, spreading the word about conservation, and showing young people around the world how to care for Earth's creatures with love and respect. I had tons of wild ideas about how to accomplish these things, and I couldn't wait to hit the ground running! But I knew that making my dreams come true couldn't only be about the emotions I felt. Sure, passion was pumping through my veins, but I had to sit back and do my homework first. There's a right way and a wrong way to have an encounter with an animal. So I needed to meet the right people, learn the proper skills, and research the best places to have these life-changing experiences. Knowledge is power, and I knew that educating myself with facts and surrounding myself with terrific teachers was the key to realizing my dreams.

I love all animals, but I've been completely obsessed with a few in particular for as long as I can remember. One was the wolverine, the ferocious, phantomlike member of the weasel family who I discovered in first grade and dreamed about meeting every day after. Another was the snapping turtle, the fierce reptile in my backyard pond whose dragon-like features captured my imagination and stoked my thirst for adventure. Then there was the great white shark, the terror-inducing, sharp-toothed predator who led me to watch *Jaws* over and over till I'd committed every line and heart-pounding scene to memory. But before I knew about any of these fascinating creatures, there was one animal who I fell in love with at the age of five. Hailing as one of the largest marine predators on our planet, this animal inspired me at such a young age that its legend and majesty will be part of me forever. For Coyote Peterson, the undisputed ruler of the seas who shaped my dreams and changed the course of my life is the one and only killer whale!

From birth to the age of eighteen, I lived in a tiny town set against the rural backdrop of northeastern Ohio, and there wasn't much to do in the summers. For my friends and me, the days pretty much went something like this: wake up, eat breakfast, and rush to the cul-de-sac to continue our never-ending game of street baseball *or* venture into the woods to explore the swamps for frogs, water snakes, and turtles before we all got called home for dinner. Day in and day out, for nearly three months of summer, this was life. Then, as you may know if you read *Brave Adventures: Volume One*, when I was in middle school, my mom bought a truck and camper, and we traveled around the country, exploring national parks. But what did I do when I wasn't playing street ball, catching critters, or traveling the country? I was reading about all the animals I dreamed of one day seeing. Yes, you read that right: *I was reading*!

You may not realize it, but you're lucky to be growing up in a time when pretty much all the information you'll ever need is just a click away. I'm not saying I lived in the Dark Ages, but information wasn't at my fingertips the way it is now. When I was a kid, the internet didn't exist, and if I wanted to learn about something like killer whales, I had to check out books from the local library, read the old encyclopedias my mom kept in her art studio, or wait for my next copy of *Zoobooks* to arrive in the mail. These print-and-paper resources helped grow my appreciation for these amazing animals and led me to dream that one day, maybe—just maybe—I might meet a killer whale out in the ocean, in its natural environment. But it's a dream that I cultivated with study and research. It took me many years, but when we launched the Brave Wilderness channel, I decided very early on that we should do an episode on killer whales. The encounter needed to happen naturally in the wild, and our goal would be to highlight the ongoing conservation projects helping protect this species.

Killer whales go by many different names, including "blackfish" and "orca." With males weighing between eight thousand and twelve thousand pounds, and females between three thousand and six thousand pounds, they're considered the largest species in the dolphin family. To be clear, all dolphins are whales, but not all whales are dolphins. So the name "killer whale" is technically correct, and while it is very common, I prefer to call them orcas. But are these ruthless, cunning hunters a threat to humans? Not at all! Despite being one of the most intelligent and powerful predators in the ocean—capable of killing even great white sharks—orcas are surprisingly docile with humans, and there has never been a recorded attack on a human in the wild.

In early 2017, Mario made contact with a company called Outer Island Excursions, which runs fishing charters and whale-watching trips out of Orcas Island, the largest of Washington's beautiful San Juan Islands. And while no one can ever guarantee seeing whales in the wild, they boasted an incredible rate of success. Seeing orcas was obviously the top priority, yet what really swayed us was their mission to promote the conservation of this species, and their drive to educate the public about what threatens orcas' existence. Both of these factors combined gave us the confidence that this was the right team to lead us in the creation of an incredible episode.

Orcas Island is part of an archipelago of over one hundred twenty islands located in the northwest corner of Washington, approximately one hundred miles northwest of Seattle and due east of Vancouver Island. Home to about five thousand people on its fifty-seven square miles, its rocky shoreline, towering fir trees, and deep, rugged fjords represent the Pacific Northwest at

perhaps its most dramatic. But much of the splendor of Orcas Island lies just off its banks, in a body of water known as the Salish Sea. Throughout its interconnected waterways, king salmon, halibut, red rock crab, sea lions, otters, and humpback whales make their homes, while bald eagles and a plethora of shore birds soar overhead. But, as its name suggests, the island may be best known for the local orcas, who migrate from the northern coast of British Columbia to as far south as Seattle, staying active throughout spring and summer in the straits that run north of Orcas Island.

Unfortunately, orcas were classified as endangered under

the Federal Endangered Species Act in 2005. The Chinook, or king salmon, of which they eat one hundred to three hundred pounds of per day, are dwindling in population due to an influx of nutrient-poor warm water into the Salish Sea. A rise in large commercial boat traffic through the Haro Strait, between the Vancouver and San Juan Islands, has contaminated the waters with pollutants, poisoning many marine inhabitants, and making it harder for orcas to find prey. Altogether, these issues have led to no calves being born in the Salish Sea in the last three years, and their numbers have dropped dramatically over the last few decades. What's even more heart-wrenching is the fact these gorgeous, sentient beings aren't just failing to reproduce; they're also starving to death. This is why I'd be so honored to see them in the wild and help promote local conservation initiatives.

Our captain and owner-operator of the charter company, Beau Brandow—affectionately nicknamed Papa Beau, referencing his love for the film *The Life Aquatic with Steve Zissou*—wanted to live up to his company's reputation.

"I've kept my ear to the ground and talked to other boat captains and tour companies all week," he said, removing the signature red skullcap he and his crew always wore in tribute to the crew of the *Belafonte*. "I know that a pod's been spotted over the past few days, but just to be on the safe side, I'll call you tomorrow morning and let you know if the first group out has seen it."

"Sounds great, Papa Beau!" I answered, barely concealing

how excited I was. I'd been waiting my whole life to see an orca in the wild, and now I was so close!

Killer whales live and hunt in groups that are known as *pods*, which are extended family networks comprised of thirty to forty animals. Within each pod are subpods that are usually centered around older females like grandmothers or even great-grandmothers. Young orcas stay connected to these pods for life, communicating with all their family members through a series of sounds that can travel up to ten miles underwater. Scientists have discovered that each pod has a distinct dialect, which is

highly unusual among animals except for humans, harbor seals, and some primates. This also puts them at the top of the list in terms of intelligence!

Just thinking about these epic aquatic creatures kept me up long past my bedtime, and when I woke up the next morning to the sound of my phone buzzing, I just knew it was Papa Beau.

"Good news, Coyote," Beau said. "A pod of about thirty to forty animals has been spotted—round up your team and meet me at the docks as soon as you can."

Mark, Mario, and photographer Austin Trigg all scarfed down their breakfasts, grabbed their gear, and together we drove the few miles to a dock on the extreme northern tip of the island. Orcas are most active in the morning, so we had no time to waste. As we arrived, we greeted the crew, busy preparing Beau's boat, the *Blackfish*, for a day out on the Salish Sea.

I was so excited upon arrival that I jumped out of our vehicle and went running down the dock toward the waiting vessel.

"This is it! The moment we've been waiting for!" I said as Beau, Bobby, and Jason finished loading the bright-yellow kayaks and gear onto the *Blackfish*. I was anxious to see one of the ocean's most legendary predators, a moment I'd been dreaming about since I was five years old!

Once we motored away from the dock and into the open ocean, our plan was to look for dorsal fins or blowhole spouts breaching the surface. As soon as we detected these indicators of orca activity, Beau would bring the boat to a stop. While Mario

Chapter 7 / Surrounded by Killer Whales!

and Austin stayed on board filming, Mark and I would head out on the water in sea kayaks with two crew members, Bobby and Jason. "How far are we going?" I asked Papa Beau after I climbed up a ladder to the top level of the *Blackfish*, where our intrepid captain was steering the boat out of the marina.

"We're going a ways out," he answered. "Probably forty miles."

We'd be almost to Canada, if not *in* Canada!

North of Orcas Island lies the Strait of Georgia, part of the Salish Sea that cuts between Washington and Canada's Vancouver Island. Since this large waterway is inland, it's sheltered from most of the rough weather patterns that hit the Pacific coast, which I found surprising based on the turbulent water we were motoring through. Keeping my eyes peeled for signs of orcas, I squinted off into the horizon, the bright sun illuminating the choppy waters before me. As we passed a collection of small islands dotting the sea behind us, my gaze swept down off the boat, stopping abruptly on the whirlpool-like swirling currents surrounding our boat. Rough waters indeed! Clearly, that was not where we'd be getting off the boat to search for whales!

"This could be an area to look for orcas," I said to the camera. "However, we cannot bring the kayaks out into water like this because Captain Beau tells me it will literally suck you down about a hundred feet into the water...never to be seen again!"

Forty miles came and went, and after a few hours of searching, we'd crossed the invisible line between US and Canadian waters. As we finally reached a calm spot, he slowed the boat to a crawl, and we prepared the kayaks for the next part of our expedition. He assured us that he had good information that the pod was close, noting that this was a confirmed area where they were known to feed. The sun was now high in the sky, and even though it was starting to get warm, I had goose bumps all over my body as an electric excitement coursed through me.

My heart was pounding as I stepped off the boat into the front seat of my kayak, and it wasn't just because I was raring to go. As I settled into my seat, the movement of the ocean rocking me swiftly side to side, small waves crashed unpredictably around me, sending cold, salty spray in every direction. I realized that this water was unlike anything I'd ever been in. More than that, it could have been a thousand feet deep, for all I knew. And what if there were dozens of hungry whales right under my kayak? Sure, I knew they were nonaggressive toward humans, but who's to say that they wouldn't accidentally flip over my kayak with a curious bump of their fins?! The kayak wasn't much wider than a sea lion, and from below the surface with oars in the water, could an orca tell the difference between the two? These are the kinds of questions that flood your mind as you are getting into a kayak to paddle in the presence of orcas!

Realistically, though, it was unlikely that we would be getting that close to them. There are strict regulations about how humans can interact with orcas: Leisure boats, commercial vessels, and kayakers are not allowed to deliberately get closer than two hundred yards away from any individual. However, if you're out paddling and see a pod of orcas off in the distance, you can stay put, hoping that they'll continue their path and swim right by you. Orcas are incredibly curious animals, as is often the case with all dolphin species, and they will investigate anything unfamiliar in their environment. Humans in floating fiberglass vessels are no exception. As Jason and I paddled ourselves away from the *Blackfish*, I mounted a GoPro at the end of our kayak to capture all the action.

Chapter 7 / Surrounded by Killer Whales!

Much to my surprise, the paddling wasn't as difficult as I imagined it would be, but we weren't having much luck spotting orcas. We'd been on the water heading north with the tide for what felt like hours. The *Blackfish* was so far back in the distance that fighting against the current to return would be nearly impossible, and if we wanted to be picked up, we'd have to radio back to Papa Beau. We would probably have a better chance of being swept into shore than paddling back to our vessel.

"Coyote, you see anything?" Mark yelled across the water from his boat.

"Nothing yet." I shrugged.

It was irrelevant small talk. It felt like we'd been paddling for hours, but we hadn't seen anything but the crests of waves. The initial excitement of getting on the water to film orcas was quickly transforming into discouragement. Soaking wet, freezing cold, and dangerously distant from the *Blackfish*, everything about our situation was telling us to radio in for pickup, and that this probably wasn't going to be our day. I turned back to look at Jason, prepared to give him the sign to radio the *Blackfish*. It was in that very moment, however, that everything changed.

Scanning the horizon one last time with a pair of binoculars, Jason noticed a black dorsal fin rise just above the water in the distance, and he called out...ORCA!

"Orcas, I see orcas....They're about two hundred yards away," he said, "so let's stop right here."

We sat in silence for several moments, watching and waiting

with focused anticipation. Our eyes scanned the rolling surface as we bore witness to the incoming pod of giants. Resisting the urge to plunge my paddle into the water to get closer, I sat tight. *If my dream of seeing an orca up close in the wild is really going to come true*, I thought, *then I've got to use the knowledge I have and let them come to me.* Patience was once again proving to pay off, as the orcas were coming straight for us and were now less than a hundred yards away. The dream was coming true!

I pulled out my little waterproof JVC camera and held it out over the kayak, my gaze fixed on the water while I adjusted the focus to clearly capture that magical moment when the pod breached the surface and swam past us. I couldn't see them, but I could sense their presence, and in that instant, time seemed

to stand still. I remember looking toward Mark to see which direction his camera was aimed, then I held my breath. *Stay focused, Coyote, you can't miss this shot,* I said to myself as a steady stream of adrenaline coursed through my body.

"Jason, you see anything back there?" I called to my boatmate.

"It's beautiful conditions, and I've heard a few blows," he said with a note of expectation in his voice. "I think there are some whales up ahead, and…it looks like there might be some right behind us!" he exclaimed, the anticipation rising in his voice.

Just then, as though on cue…*Whoosh!* A gleaming black body the size of a bus breached the water's surface and let out a long, forceful blast from its spout. There it was! I couldn't contain my excitement.

"Didja see that?!" I yelled to Mark as my eyes raced across the dancing waves for the next splash. "Woo! That was awesome!" No sooner had I spoken those last words than another whale broke through the water.

As if a thousand fireworks exploded in the sky all at once, a huge, dramatic jet-black torpedo rose from the depths, rocketing out of the sea. Its full body hung in the air and then, in classic orca fashion, slammed back down into the waves, displacing water in every direction. *Crash!* I couldn't believe what I was seeing! My camera captured every frame as a warmth filled my heart, and waves of kinetic energy zipped through the air and directly into my being. My adrenaline was surging as I held my camera over the side of the kayak, my mouth broken into a wide, ecstatic grin.

Chapter 7 / Surrounded by Killer Whales!

"Oh wow, I've got an orca right here!" I screamed. "That was awesome!"

For several moments dorsal fins and blowholes erupted from the ocean waves as the pod adjusted course to investigate our humble bobbing vessels. Suddenly, the same orca from the first jump burst from the water and turned on its side, revealing the stark contrast between its black fins and upper body, and white belly. It tossed itself up into the air, then smacked its smooth sides against the surface with a massive, earthshaking *splash!* As it disappeared into the depths of the sea around us, I felt a warm sense of satisfaction and calm blanket my mind.

There I was, out in the middle of the water, surrounded by one of the ocean's top predators, yet I didn't feel fear. These huge, fierce animals have jaws armed with up to fifty-two conical teeth that are capable of ripping a shark in half, yet I was almost in a daydream, completely at peace. As beautiful golden sunlight cascaded across the waves, I felt the fatigue from paddling for hours leave my body, replaced by a sense of unity with the glorious orca I'd just seen, wild and free in its natural habitat. Deep down, a part of me suspected that there was absolutely no way life could ever get any better than this...but I was wrong!

Suddenly, all around me, the pod of orcas began to surface once again, shooting water from their spouts, circling left to right, and gliding through the waves side by side. As soon as one dove, another appeared, on and on like a waterwheel, speeding through the sea. This was incredible! Were they hunting? Not for us! Orcas hunt through precision, timing, and strategy, working in a group to attack a school of salmon or a family of seals from multiple angles. They patiently surround an animal, wait for their chance to close in, and use the power of the pod to immobilize their target. The porpoises knock the animal back and forth, altering the current and sending vibrations through the water disorient and confuse it. Then they seize the opportunity to move in and devour their meal. *That is* not *what's about to happen here*, I said to myself. *These orcas are playing, acting curious, and just having fun. I'm simply lucky to be a part of their world.*

"This is amazing!" I said to the camera. "We are surrounded by orcas right now!"

I'd estimate we were within one hundred fifty yards of the pod at their farthest point, and I was so ecstatic I could have leaped from my kayak, but I held steady, eyes darting around

me, camera at the ready, waiting for the next moment of encounter. Then, at a distance of roughly two hundred yards, a wide, glistening body ascended to the surface. It was enormous, splitting the waves in both directions with great power and more force than any orca sweeping past us. Its long dorsal fin extended straight up, menacingly, like the shark's in *Jaws*, and right away I could tell that this was not only the biggest orca yet, but it was a male.

"There he is," I whispered. Everything around me was silent except a stray splash and the whoosh of air escaping from the orca's blowhole. Then a disbelieving voice broke my reverie.

"That's coming right at us," said Mark.

With my camera focused, I watched with split attention, one eye on the actual animal, the other eye on the screen to make sure I was keeping the shot lined up. I could feel my pulse pumping all the way through my fingertips. Then, just when it seemed we would collide, the orca swerved away from the kayak and disappeared back into the water. *Whoosh!* It resurfaced behind us, and with a great bellow, it blasted through the waves again with a misty blow of air. It joined the rest of the pod, still splashing and bounding all around us, as they swam past our kayaks and back out to the open sea.

"That was awesome!" I yelled. It was as magical a moment as I have ever had in nature, and I wished it could last forever. For over twenty or so spectacular, life-changing minutes, I'd watched a pod of wild orcas swim, breach, and play in the expanse of ocean they loved the most. We waited in silence, hands clenched to our cameras and oars, hoping to capture just one more dramatic moment, but the giants were nowhere to be seen. Just as quickly as the orcas had appeared…they were gone.

As Jason, Bobby, Mark, and I paddled back to the *Blackfish*, I came to realize that a childhood dream had unfolded around me. I'd experienced a true connection with the environment and one of its most marvelous aquatic species, fully grasping the magnitude, beauty, wisdom, intelligence, and power that defines these timeless animals as the rulers of the sea. But this didn't happen by accident. I was inspired as a child, and I followed that curiosity up with research and determination. I did my homework, pursued my dream, and in the end, I found myself submerged in the environment with one of the world's most beloved animals.

The team and I recounted the day's action as the *Blackfish* carried us back to harbor. Warm setting sunlight enveloped the vessel, and we were saturated in a seemingly endless glow. Although this adventure was coming to a close, it will stand out in my memory as an incredible hard-earned dream that was more fulfilling than I could have ever imagined. The killer whale, the blackfish, the orca...no matter how you choose to address this majestic animal, it is undoubtedly the top predator of the world's oceans. I hope that with this video, and subsequently this chapter, I've helped create a better understanding of orcas, and that you, too, will work to create a better world for them to live in. Their elegance and beauty are unmatched in the animal kingdom, and when you see a family pod in the wild, their presence touches your heart in a way that can't be described with words. I know that for as long as I live, I will never forget the first moment I witnessed that black dorsal fin cutting through the waves, and the *thrill* of how it felt to be in the presence of orcas.

Chapter Eight
The Elusive Sand Monitor!

Chapter 8 / The Elusive Sand Monitor!

As you've probably learned, making your dreams come true can be hard work, and sometimes you have no choice but to go all in, expending the kind of energy you never knew you had. Every person who's summited Mount Everest has faced the threat of frostbite and overcome stifled gasps of thin air; every gold medal–winning Olympic athlete has trained through cramped, aching muscles and fought fatigue; and every great scientist has mastered the art of working long, sleepless all-nighters. As the saying goes, if there's no pain, there's no gain—a reality that was never more appropriate than when I traveled to Australia to make my most epic reptilian catch ever: a lightning-fast apex predator known as the sand monitor!

The continent of Australia is anchored by its heavily populated coastal cities, including Sydney, Melbourne, Brisbane, and Perth. Far beyond those metropolises, though, in the heart of its interior, is a vast, remote, unpopulated wilderness known as the Outback. With long stretches of arid land in its center, thousands upon thousands of acres of grassy pastures at its edges, and rainy tropical regions blanketing the north, the Outback remains one of the world's largest, most intact and unspoiled wilderness areas. Here, red kangaroos and dingoes roam freely, flocks of cockatoos, bee-eaters, and wedge-tailed eagles make their nests, and hundreds of species of reptiles soak up the relentlessly scorching sun.

To get to our chosen destination, Mark, Mario, and I traversed long red-dirt roads, driving for hours with scarcely another traveler in sight. To find an elusive animal, you have to venture into its natural habitat, which in this case was in the middle of nowhere. There was no doubt in my mind that our endeavors would pay off, and as we drew closer to the tiny dot on our map called Meandarra, I could see a few vestiges of civilization come into view. *I can't wait to meet a monitor!* I thought, as an image of a cartoon scoundrel drifted into my mind.

Like so many of my favorite animal species, I've been fascinated by monitor lizards since I was a kid. One Saturday afternoon, my mom, sister, and I went to see a Disney movie called *The Rescuers Down Under*, which starred the fearless, crime-solving mice Bernard and Bianca as they traveled to the Australian Outback to rescue a little boy in peril. The villain of the film was a poacher, and his sidekick was a crafty reptile named Joanna the Goanna—*goanna* being the common name for the highly intelligent lizard known as the monitor. Most Americans, especially little boys in rural Ohio, aren't very familiar with monitors, so I started to read up on them and I quickly became hooked for life.

There are seventy-nine species of monitor lizards living throughout Africa, Asia, the Pacific Islands, and Australia, and they include the world's largest lizard, the Komodo dragon; the aquatic Nile monitor; and the sleek, nomadic Perentie monitor. Known for their distinctive long tails and necks, muscular bodies, forked tongues, and curved, talon-like claws, I always thought that monitor lizards were the most dinosaur-like

reptiles out there. Of course,
dinosaurs evolved into
birds, not reptiles, but the
fact is that these lizards
resemble these prehistoric
beasts so much that when
filmmakers were designing
velociraptors for the movie *Jurassic Park*, they

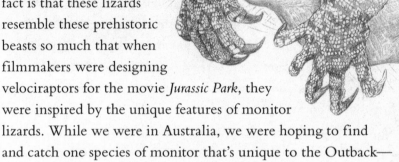

were inspired by the unique features of monitor
lizards. While we were in Australia, we were hoping to find
and catch one species of monitor that's unique to the Outback—
the sand monitor—which is called *bungarra* or *tangka* in some
native languages, or more commonly, the sand goanna.

Scccreeee! Our truck rolled to a stop and I snapped out of
my daydream. I got out and looked over the rustic Royal Hotel
Meandarra, our home away from home for the next several
days. Two hundred and fifty miles northwest of Brisbane, and
nestled on the eastern edge of the Outback, it was surrounded
by open country on all sides—a perfect place to set out in the
true wild of the bush. Before we could get started, Mario, Mark,
and I planned to meet up with two awesome blokes named Max
and Lockie at the local inn. We needed guides and found two
homegrown Aussies with expertise in native reptiles who run a
series of wilderness experience tours called Australian Wildlife
Encounters. We met them the day we arrived, and talked late
into the evening, plotting our mission for the days to come.

Our tactic was rather simple: You literally ride in the vehicle while looking out the window with the hope of eventually spotting a large lizard. Like all their reptilian cousins, sand monitors are ectothermic and rely on the sun for energy. So we were hoping to spot them basking either in the middle of the sun-drenched road or perched upon the adjacent embankments. Monitors prefer areas with sandy soil and rocky outcroppings— rather than hard, parched desert—because that's where they seek refuge when the sun is scarce and temperatures drop. By digging burrows or commandeering them from other animals, they're able to keep warm at night and through the winter months. If we could find one, I knew catching it would be a difficult task, as monitor lizards are notoriously speedy. The best journeys are usually the most challenging, so I was ready to give my all when we finally found our target.

Chapter 8 / The Elusive Sand Monitor!

Meandarra is a blip on the map of Australia, right in the middle of the true wilderness that locals call "the bush." With a population of just under four hundred, it's a bit like a ghost town. In the middle of the day, you could stand in the center of the township's main road, turn in every direction and not see a single person or car. This is exactly why Max and Lockie wanted this to be our meeting place. Under wide-open, sunny blue skies, the heat beating down on its flat, unpaved roads, Meandarra provided a perfect location for base camp in our search for monitors. Knowing the area like the back of their hands, Max and Lockie confirmed that we'd have a pretty good chance of finding one basking in the morning sun before setting out to hunt for other lizards, snakes, birds, bird eggs, or small mammals.

The next morning, our guides picked us up just after breakfast. We piled into their cars, with Mario, Mark, Max, and I in one car, and Lockie following behind in another. Max and Lockie knew the lizards' favorite basking areas well, so we started driving, dirt and dust kicking up in every direction as narrow, spindly trees whizzed past our windows. Now, this wasn't the iconic Outback you might be thinking of, a vast expanse of reddish-orange dirt covering what looks like the surface of Mars, and the giant rock known as Uluru, looming on the horizon. But it was still rugged, breathtaking, and mysterious, with vast grazing fields of dry, green grass, and dense tangles of underbrush. We drove west for miles and miles and *miles*, deep into the bush, and any evidence of humans disappeared completely. On this seemingly never-ending stretch, there were no houses, no stop signs, no other cars...not even any other roads! It was truly the middle of nowhere, as far as the eye could see. Finally, after a few hours, I spied the slender body of a reptile.

"Guys, there's something there!" I yelled, craning my neck over Mario's shoulder as my eyes zeroed in on a long, lean form that stretched partially across the dirt road, about fifty yards in front of our car. "Let's get out!"

Fully aware that this creature could dart away at any second, I crept toward it, gaining speed when I realized it took notice. The lizard zig-zagged into the grass, looked back at me, and made a feeble attempt at concealing itself under a thicket of weeds. It really didn't seem too bothered, because as I crouched down, rustling leaves and snapping twigs, it didn't hightail away. I paused and studied it. This reptile was light grayish-brown with sparse bands, not dark olive like the monitor lizard. Its rounded head and squat, streamlined body were supported by four tiny legs, sticking out of its sides as its belly and neck lay on the dirt. *That's not how a sand monitor stands*, I thought, my heart sinking. *They hold their heads up high.* Then I saw the telltale sign that confirmed my doubts. *Flip.* The lizard stuck out its round, slug-like tongue, and I noticed its very distinctive bright-blue coloration. *Darn it! That's a blue-tongued skink!*

This common yet unique Australian lizard was a beauty, but it was not the reptile we were looking for. I wanted to catch a monitor lizard! That being said, I couldn't pass up the opportunity to admire this scaly creature, so I gently scooped it up, its mouth agape, flashing its vibrant blue tongue. After snapping a few pictures, I set the lizard back on the ground and watched as its smooth and agile body slithered just like a snake into the bush. Skinks are often mistaken for snakes in the Australian backcountry, and they fooled us several times over the course of the day. At one point, Max brought the car to a screeching halt when we saw a medium-size, dark-brown lizard on the side of the road. But when I lowered my window, I noticed the large flap of spikey skin just below its neck and along its sides. *That's an eastern bearded dragon*, I said to myself, *not a monitor lizard!*

"Don't worry, we'll see one soon," Max assured us. "They may be elusive, but trust me, they really are everywhere. It's just a matter of being in the right place at the right time."

We were several hours into our road trip, but I wasn't letting my mind drift. I was laser-focused on my dream of catching a monitor, remembering all the reasons they captivated me. One of them was the intelligent way they create nests. Monitor lizards will roam the bush looking for termite mounds, dig into them, then lay their eggs inside, so the heat generated by the mound will help with incubation. Not only that, but the termites will continue to build their nest back on top, coincidently helping protect the eggs from predators.

The sun was at its highest point in the sky, and my head was spinning with dreams of this fascinating lizard when Mark perked up. Had he seen something on the side of the road?

"Monitor right there," he said, extending his pointed finger into the front seat, where I was now sitting. As we sped past, I craned my neck around, following the dark shape behind us. I squinted, trying to make out its features. *Okay, I see it*, I said to myself. *And its body is long, it's holding its head up high, and its tail is twice the length of its body! That is most definitely a monitor!*

"Hurry, turn the car around!" I yelled to Max. "It's right up there on that edge. This is it, guys!"

I was determined to do whatever it took to catch a monitor, and I was well prepared. I had a GoPro strapped to my shoulder to capture the first-person perspective of the action since both hands would be necessary to catch this reptile. From what I'd heard from Max, I knew I'd have to run, so I'd made sure my boots were tied tight. But what I wasn't fully prepared for was just how fast these lizards truly are. Our truck rolled about ten feet away from the monitor, and I carefully opened the passenger door, ready to leap toward it. Upon seeing me, the monitor dug its sharp, curved claws into the ground, lowered its head, and darted into the brush so fast I could hardly see where it went.

My feet hit the ground at a run, as I made my way toward the edge of the bush. I heard a rustle in the dry grasses next to the road and sprinted toward them, crouching down as I approached the underbrush where I thought the speedster might be hunkered down. I peered beneath the tangles of weeds and logs, but all was quiet. I'd lost it.

"It got down into a burrow," I said to the camera. "There wasn't a chance of catching that one."

The truth was that this reptile had sped away so fast I couldn't even be sure it was a sand monitor as opposed to some other kind of monitor lizard. From a distance, most monitor species look the same, so it could have been a yellow-throated monitor or a lace monitor—either of which I would have been thrilled to catch!

Late into the afternoon, as the sun dipped behind the scraggily branches of tall, narrow trees, I felt as if we'd been driving on the same dirt road for days. Every twisting hardwood—nestled within a tinderbox of fallen branches—looked the same; every mile-long stretch of parched yellow pasture seemed like something I'd seen two hours before. The cloud-covered sky stretched so far that, if I stared up, I got lost in it. My eyes were exhausted from scanning back and forth, and my head was spinning from watching the same scene pass by the truck's windows. I wanted to lean back in my seat and shut my eyes until I heard Max speak up.

"Monitor up ahead."

I shook my head and quickly looked out the windshield.

Long tail and body—check. Head high and at an angle—check. Strong, muscular legs extended out on both sides—yes, sir. This was most definitely a monitor! "Right there, right there," I answered. "Slow down!"

The truck came to a stop, and I got out to inch toward the now-wary reptile, my boots crunching in the gravel. It was right in the middle of the road, looking at me as if to say, *Just try to catch me, Coyote Peterson. Just try.* Unlike the earlier encounter, I realized I had an ideal situation on my hands. Max and Lockie had said that sometimes monitors won't move when a person approaches, as if they're holding their ground, expecting you to feel intimidated by their size and stature and ultimately turn around and walk the other way. Instead, it gives someone like me the perfect chance to pounce. So I moved deliberately, step by step, toward it, till I was about ten feet away.

Zoom! Like a bullet from the barrel of a gun, the sand monitor whipped its body around and took off so fast I struggled to even follow its path visually. *Oh my gosh...there it goes!* Truth be told, I was caught off guard, but I quickly regained my composure and snapped into action, breaking into a sprint, like a flash into the underbrush. I could hear the sound of the lizard speeding off as it gained noticeable distance from me. Jumping over fallen tree trunks, hurtling mounds of grasses, and using low-hanging branches as springboards to launch me farther into the bush, I kept in close pursuit. I felt like a character in a video game, leaping from one obstacle to the next, while hoping to not misjudge a jump and land on the ground. *Splat. Game over!*

To this day, several things amaze me about this crazy monitor chase I'd embarked on. The first was that I didn't stumble over a branch, falling face first into a briar patch. The second was that the escapee didn't scramble down a burrow, where we'd never be able to reach it. But the third was that Mark, Mario, and I were keeping pace with it, even a full minute into running! This lizard might have been fast, but we could see every sharp turn and cloud of dust as it tried to shake its pursuers.

We knew we'd be out of luck if the chase ended underground, but what if the elusive reptile shot straight up a tree? Monitors are known climbers, using their razor-sharp claws and strong limbs to dig into a trunk and scale it. They can climb just about any tree in the bush! Would it be the end of the road, or just another obstacle? We'd just have to find out!

"See it?" Mark asked, stopping finally to take a breath. "It's right up in that tree."

Sure enough, this reptile, with its skilled climbing ability, had scampered about thirty to thirty-five feet up a eucalyptus tree and was now perched on a limb.

Those of you out there who regularly watch the Brave Wilderness channel know that I love to climb trees. I have this uncanny repto-mammalian ability to grab on to all kinds of trunks—those with branches, those without, skinny trees, fat trees, whatever!—and scurry up them using the grip of my thighs and my upper body strength. Yes, Coyote Peterson is part monkey, and when I stood at the base of the tree that the monitor had climbed, I knew I had no choice but to go up after it. Sure, it had no branches I could grab on to, but it was at a slight angle, giving me an advantage when I hoisted myself up.

I was rather confident in my abilities, but climbing thirty-five feet? That's another story! I looked up at the lizard, taunting me as it swept its long tail over the side of its perch. *Don't hesitate, Coyote,* I said to myself. *If there's no pain, there's no gain!* Putting my hands on the rough, ridged bark of the tree, I took a deep breath, bent my legs, and tapped into the reserve of strength I'd been storing up all day to jump up and grab on with all four limbs. Holding the trunk between my thighs, I threw my arms up a foot, then hugged the sturdy column with all the strength in my upper body as I heaved my legs up with short lunge. Have you ever seen a bear climb a tree? That's what it looked like from the ground…a bear with a cowboy hat!

I shimmied about twenty feet up the textured bark until the tree split, and I found a few branches I could grip. I had my eyes locked on the lizard, and briefly repositioned myself on the limb where it had taken refuge. The monitor, realizing it was still being pursued, climbed even higher up and out onto the limb of the tree, ducking out of my line of sight. I knew the reptile *had* to be there, but its distinctive dark grayish-brown coloration acted as camouflage, and no matter how far I stretched my neck, I couldn't tell the lizard apart from the bark.

"It's on the end of that branch," Max said from down below. I was now wrapped around the same upright limb, balancing precariously as I scooted forward, trusting that the rascally reptile would soon come into view. I kept my body low like a leopard would, and steadily inched my way closer until...*There you are!* The tip of the monitor's tail stuck out awkwardly and blew its cover.

You've got nowhere to go, buddy, I thought. *I'm the only way out of this predicament!*

Finally, the limb started to level out, and I paused to catch my breath. Luckily, the wood was thick enough to support my weight; Coyotes aren't very heavy. Otherwise, the reptile I was chasing and I would fall about thirty-five feet straight down with a...*Snap! Crack! Foom!* I tried not to think about the possibility or the mangled mess I might become. I had to keep my mind in the moment, but I couldn't help looking down. Mark, Mario, Max, and Lockie looked like miniature people down below me, and I can promise you it was terrifying!

I felt my heart pounding in my throat, but I took a deep breath, harnessed my courage, and balanced against the limb with my thigh. I was just out of reach of its sweeping tail, so I grasped a nearby branch and gained a few inches as I positioned my other leg on a firm foothold to my right. The lizard was turned away from me, so my only hope of snagging it was to grasp the base of its tail. This is where the second hazard flashed into my mind: Monitor lizards are so agile that it was possible

this one might twist itself around and grab me with a mouthful of sharp teeth, ripping my arm to shreds!

Some lizards, like geckos and skinks, have a special defense mechanism, in which they are capable of dropping or releasing their tails, giving them an opportunity to escape predators or potential capture. That wasn't the case with this species. Once it's been seized, a sand monitor's response isn't escape; it's attack! Behind their streamlined faces are two rows of teeth, like miniature razor blades, all of which are hooked backward. When they strike at another lizard, a small mammal, a bird—

or, in this case, Coyote Peterson—they bite, shake, and tear tissue into ribbons, as if you've just put your hand into a paper shredder. Needless to say, I was nervous, but I swallowed my doubts and readjusted my grip. With all my might, I lunged, my arm outstretched, palm wide open, fingers searching for the scaly creature just within my reach.

When I grabbed the monitor's tail with my left hand, the angry reptile lurched forward in an attempt to flee my grip and dug into the tree bark with its birdlike claws. I pulled firmly in an attempt to slide the animal back as it leaped, close enough to get control of its middle, while I clung to the tree with my legs, holding on for dear life.

The monitor was losing its composure, and instead of stubbornly sheltering in place, it began flailing, jerking my arm with every jolt and jostle of its body. This was quickly becoming one of the most precarious catch scenarios I had ever found myself in, but I was not about to let go. *Chrt skrt chit!* Suddenly, it detached from its hold. *Now's my chance!* I thought. I deliberately swung the critter to a smaller cluster of branches, bringing it within reach of my right hand. My window of opportunity to pull off this miraculous catch was closing; it was now or never! With a burst of precisely calculated force, I grabbed the monitor just behind the head with my free hand and seized control of the rowdy reptile.

"Got it!" I yelled down to the crew below.

"That might be your most epic catch of all time!" answered Mark.

It sure was, and it was perhaps my hardest, too! But big goals require a mountain of effort, and as the monitor wrapped its arms and legs around me, digging its talon-like claws into my skin, I knew the hardest part was yet to come.

"Now the question is, how I'm going to get back down?!" I yelled.

I hoped that positioning my hand and forearm under the lizard, cradling its chest while grasping its neck from underneath, would keep it from wriggling free. But would I be able to slide down the tree, holding on with just one arm? I'd have to try!

"Ohhhh! Owww!" I yelled as I descended, scraping my forearms, chafing my legs, and rubbing my shirt uncomfortably against my chest. But in less than a minute I had made it back down, leaping from the trunk on the last stretch and landing with a powerfully confident thud on the ground.

Chapter 8 / The Elusive Sand Monitor!

"That is how you climb a tree to catch a monitor!" I yelled, barely able to catch my breath. I gave Mark a big high five as the entire team celebrated this unbelievably epic moment. Now it was time to show the world one of the fastest, most cunning reptiles in Australia, and I couldn't have been more excited!

As beautiful sunbeams streamed through the trees at that magical, close-to-sunset time we call "the Golden Hour," I looked closely at the monitor, gaining a true appreciation for the form and beauty of this lizard. Judging by its size, this one was most likely young male. At just about three feet long, it certainly wasn't the biggest sand monitor I could have found (they average about four and a half feet), but its tiny, spectacled scales made it truly unique and spectacular in my mind.

"I tell you what," I said, staring into the goanna's sharp, orangey-brown eyes, which seemed to hold a certain wisdom. "These creatures are intelligent; like, almost problem-solving intelligent." It was true. An incredible amount of research has been done regarding monitor intelligence, and they have even been known to memorize shapes, patterns, and routes.

"All monitor species have a forked tongue," I continued, "that helps them navigate their environment and detect their prey. When it goes back into their mouths, similar to a Gila monster, they have what's called a Jacobson's organ in the roof of their mouth. And as the tongue runs over that organ, it tells them—almost like a little computer—*Your food is this way*, or *Your food is that way*. Or *Something is getting close in your environment that you should flee from*."

Chapter 8 / The Elusive Sand Monitor!

I still couldn't believe that I was holding this magnificent creature, and that we were both safely on hard ground. I could feel its front claws drag across my skin as the monitor posed nonthreateningly in my grasp. Amazed at their length and the power those claws could wield, I was thankful that I had barely a scratch on me, except a few chafe marks from the tree. I turned the lizard so that its back was facing the camera, admiring the incredible strength this animal possessed.

"It is holding on to me as tightly as I am holding on to it. Look at that; it is locked into place. There is so much muscle structure in the tail and the center of its body," I said.

Then I marveled at the lizard's skin, which was leathery rather than sleek, like the blue-tongued skink's. Looking closely, you could see why it was called a *sand* monitor, as the burnt-sienna pebble-like scales on its back

transitioned to orange, yellow, and tan in clusters surrounded by a dull black. It was a veritable mosaic of color, all coming together to form circular patterns like a jaguar's spots on its legs, and cloudy alternating bands down its tail. "Look at that coloration. See all that yellow speckling along the sides of the legs and at then that yellow tip of its tail? That's one way you can easily distinguish this monitor as compared to some of the other species that are out here in the bush."

The team and I finished filming the episode, taking our time to capture on camera the best shots we possibly could. This lizard deserved all of our effort, and I truly believe it could sense our profound admiration. Monitor lizards rank as one of, if not *the*, most difficult reptiles in the world to catch. But despite their intelligence, speed, and agility always putting them several paces ahead of any pursuing admirer, my hard work and determination had paid off.

Even though the sand monitor hadn't started to squirm, I knew it was time to return this elusive predator to the wild. It wanted nothing more than to go back to a life of basking in the sun, scrambling into burrows, stealing eggs, dining on carcasses, and pushing adventurers like me to their physical and mental limits. We all said our humble good-byes, then I placed the lizard down on the ground in front of me. As I gently released my grip, it bolted from my hands in a cloud of dust, its scaly silhouette disappearing into the shadows of the underbrush.

We faced many challenges in our quest to bring this lizard up close for the cameras, inspiring me to reach an athletic level that I'd never faced with any previous reptile. Yet it was a combination of patience, teamwork, and persistence that ultimately led to our success. Sure, making it all the way out to Australia was a dream come true in and of itself, but having the chance to search for and catch a sand monitor in the Outback—a place as diverse and beautiful as you can possibly imagine— was like earning a spot in the World Series of animal catching. The sand monitor proudly stands as one of the greatest animal encounters of my career. And I consider myself fortunate to have had such an epic conclusion to the tale of my time spent in the land of lizards!

Chapter Nine
The Enormous Elephant Encounter!

Chapter 9 / The Enormous Elephant Encounter!

S ometimes the greatest adventures of your life happen by
being in the right place at the right time. Through the
last eight chapters, I have highlighted the importance
of preparation, hard work, and a bit of risk in order to fulfill
your wildest dreams. However, every once in a great while,
your dreams may manifest themselves with a bit of help from
that elusive thing called luck. When we first started the Brave
Wilderness channel, I had no idea that getting bitten, stung, or
chomped by some of the world's most feared and misunderstood
creatures would prove to be so popular and celebrated by so
many millions of thrill-seeking animal enthusiasts. Of course,
I had to put myself in this precarious position to *make* these
scenarios unfold; no one just wakes up one morning and says, *I
think I'll spend the next three years enduring a large amount of pain for
the fun of it!* As most of you know, I took almost all of these bites,
stings, and chomps intentionally with the hope of educating the
Coyote Pack about these fascinating animals. While there was
always a certain amount of luck, the creation of these wildly
popular, and in many cases "extreme," videos required a little
more strategy. But deep down inside, I was always dreaming
about much bigger adventures. The kind of timeless expeditions
that one might be pulled into instead of seeking out. These were
the moments with nature that couldn't be planned, when timing
was everything.

South Africa is the ideal place for the wonderfully
unexpected to happen. Stretching over one thousand miles from
the Atlantic to the Indian Ocean, it's a vast playground for all

kinds of wildlife, including the lumbering African buffalo, the highly venomous Cape cobra, and the mighty black rhinoceros. During my travels to the Kariega Game Reserve in the spring of 2018, I'd had the incredible fortune of going hand-to-paw with a tranquilized pride of lions. That experience gave me a new appreciation for their breathtaking majesty, and I truly grasped the understanding as to *why* they are crowned the kings of the savanna. But in our time at Kariega, there was one creature we hadn't yet featured in an episode: the African elephant. Proudly hailed as the world's largest land mammal and perhaps the most beloved creature in all of Africa, the elephants at Kariega roam freely across the vast savanna and wooded foothills of the Zuurberg Mountains. The rocky highlands are studded with thick forests of twisted trees and provide an astonishing amount of cover for even the most massive African elephants. Finding them among the vegetation would be a challenge; however, if we were in the right place at the right time, an encounter was sure to be epic.

Stretching twenty-five thousand acres across the southeastern interior of South Africa, the Kariega Game Reserve has a small population of African elephants who— along with the pride of lions—live on the predator side of the park. The most famous and formidable of these animals is a titan nicknamed the Big Tusker, and he's not just the biggest elephant at Kariega—he's also believed to be one of the largest elephants at any of South Africa's animal sanctuaries. There are two types of African elephants—the forest and savanna—and

the differences between
the two include the
fact that the savanna
elephant is bigger
and has tusks that
curve away from
each other. The
forest elephant is
smaller, and its tusks
turn inward. Standing a
staggering thirteen feet tall, the
Big Tusker is definitely a savanna
elephant, and his imposing, sharp ivory tusks curve in a way that
is so distinctive that his identity is unmistakable. But would we
find him when we set off on our search? We might—anything is
possible when you let your mind and spirit connect with nature
and go with the flow of the universe!

"You're going to have to track him down," said our
guide, Jo. "And you can do that by looking for environmental
indicators of elephant activity all around the reserve."

The plan was for Mark, Mario, and I to meet Jo early one
morning—when elephants are most active, out foraging for food
in the shrubland of the Kariega River Valley—and have her
drive us in a Land Cruiser along the reserve's unpaved roads.
Just like early explorers on an epic scouting mission, we'd search
and scour the environment for telltale clues, including large
tracks in the mud, mounds of droppings on the ground, broken

tree limbs, and, in some cases, flattened shrubs. Elephants are surprisingly elusive, and when they're not seeking out their next meal, they prefer to seek refuge in the woodlands than be exposed to the harsh elements on the savanna. Their rough gray skin blends perfectly against the dull bark of real yellowwood, assegai, and acacia trees, providing seamless camouflage for the humble giants. I was skeptical at first, thinking that elephants would be hard to miss! But Jo assured me that she knew right where to look, and while there's never a guarantee that we'd see them, we sure were going to try our best!

"During the heat of the afternoon, elephants typically hunker down in the shade and hide," Jo said as Mark, Mario, and I loaded ourselves and our gear into her Land Cruiser. "So let's try to get everything done this morning."

We were ready! We each had binoculars so we could scan the hills for trunks, ears, or tusks and look far into the treetops to see leaves and limbs rustling. If we spotted either of these things, we'd drive in that direction. Although Jo had a few reliable areas in mind for where the herd might be, the often solo Big Tusker would be harder to track down. Elephants travel miles and miles over the course of the day, so while the group had recently been spotted around the lodges where maintenance workers often left tree trimmings, they might very well be twenty miles away by now, parading along one of the many tall ridges of the sanctuary. Jo decided it was best to drive along a rugged unpaved road that led to a more expansive part of the reserve. This area, referred to as wooded lowlands and Afromontane, was an expanse of lush evergreens and steep hillsides, providing plenty of shade and cover. There among the trees, Jo thought we had a good chance of finding them feeding.

The road stretched as far as the eye could see, and beautiful grasslands that were strewn with a few spindly trees lay on either of its sides. I imagined how the elephants would cross this vast terrain before they headed into the hills to escape the heat of the day. The Land Cruiser's tires crunched on the gravel and kicked up dust as Jo downshifted, and we started to climb a ridge, the vegetation growing thicker as the road grew narrower. We bumped over foothills and along valleys, and soon the shrubs and trees lining the road were so dense that my binoculars became useless. I turned my attention toward the ground, looking for footprints or droppings.

"Look there, look there," Jo said, pointing to the road ahead as she slowed the Land Cruiser. Immediately, I saw four circular patterns in the middle of the road, each of them considerably bigger than dinner plates. These were most definitely elephant tracks!

"We've got elephant tracks there, guys. We've got to stop!" I yelled back to Mark and Mario.

Jo and I leaped out of the car at the same time and ran toward the tracks to investigate. There was no question about it; they were fresh. I hurried over to the deepest impression, stepping both feet right into the center of it. My boots didn't quite fill half of the elephant's print, and even when kneeling I barely filled the whole space. Next to me, I noticed a pile of

loose dirt on the side of the road, and I crouched down, picked
it up to see if it was moist, and let it sift through my fingers.

"Right here you can see that the elephant used its trunk to
scoop up all this loose soil, and then it would have thrown it
over its back," I said, tossing my handful of brownish-orange
dirt over my own back. "That's what they do. They cover
themselves in dust or mud to keep cool in the middle of the
day."

Believe it or not, mud and dirt also work like sunscreen to
protect the elephants' skin from the harsh rays of the sun. Talk
about being an intelligent animal! So if we found the elephant
who'd left these tracks, it was sure to be covered in dust. While
the tracks were certainly fresh, this gigantic land mammal was
nowhere in sight, indicating we had time to study the footprints
more closely. I stepped from one to
another, admiring the tremendous
size of the animal that left
them. The hind prints
were clear on
the other side of
the road, and
I stomped one
foot into each of
them, illustrating
the distance. I
was amazed; these
footprints were so

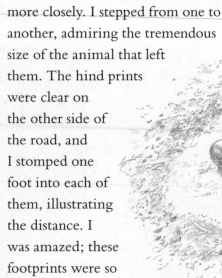

perfectly circular that it was almost as if they were staged. This was a big elephant, and in my head, I asked, *Could this possibly be the Big Tusker?!*

"The Big Tusker is usually solitary," Jo said, as if she'd been reading my mind, "so between the fact that there was only one set of tracks and that they were so massive, I have a feeling it was probably him."

We got back into the Land Cruiser and continued driving up the dusty ridge, our binoculars once again glued to our eyeballs. We didn't see any other tracks, but we did see other signs of elephant activity: droppings the size of softballs, broken branches, and large areas on the road with freshly disturbed dirt. Elephants are incredibly intelligent creatures—with brains that are structurally similar to humans—and their excellent hearing and ability to sense vibrations with their feet meant that they may have sensed our approach and retreated. So Mark, Mario, Jo, and I doubled up our elephant-spotting efforts, keeping our eyes peeled as we drove up a ridge to a high clearing, where it would be easier to scan the horizon.

That's where we struck gold!

"Stop, stop, stop!" I yelled to Jo. Through my binoculars, I focused my gaze across a clearing and up on the side of a densely wooded hill.

"See something?" asked Mark.

"Yes, I've got an elephant! Mario, see it all the way up on the top of that ridge there? It's almost silhouetted against the sky. One hundred percent, that's an elephant, and it looks big!"

We had not been detected
and we were far enough away
that only a loud noise would
alert this foraging beast of our presence. The excitement was
electric, and Mario quickly zoomed in to get a voucher shot—
basically a way to prove that *yes*, we had seen an elephant. The
animal slowly lumbered through a cluster of thick underbrush,
the outline of its back practically slicing through the dense
canopy of trees. Even at this distance, close to half a mile as the
crow flies, its size was intimidating and the ease with which it
moved was proof of its unstoppable power.

Now the real challenge had begun. Just because we could
see an elephant didn't mean we could get close enough to
film a scene with it. The distance wasn't a problem, but the
overgrown environment and lack of drivable road could cripple
our advance. How in the world were we going to get to this
elephant?! Well, it was a good thing we had Jo!

Chapter 9 / The Enormous Elephant Encounter!

Being a safari guide is all about taking calculated risks to get up close with animals, and no one at Kareiga Game Reserve was better at navigating the impossible than Jo. She would have to go off-road and up the mountainside for this one, but she was undoubtedly up for the challenge.

I wasn't nervous at all. Mark and Mario had their cameras rolling, and we were on the adventure of a lifetime with an elephant in sight. It was go time! Jo led us off the main road and across a field, where we bumped down a ditch and emerged on a seldom-used track. We followed two narrow tire lanes to the top of the foothills, and traversed several switchbacks and steep climbs, the path growing more obscured the father we went. Soon, we were hurtling up over rocks and fallen trees, ducking low-hanging branches, and plodding along the ridge where I'd spotted the gray goliath. It was a roller-coaster ride to the top, and at the highest possible point Jo cut the engine and we listened for sounds of the elephant.

The wind whistled through the tall, yellow grasses and tree branches. In the distance, I heard the faint sounds of snapping twigs, but unable to see past the dense foliage in front of us, I strained to make out the distinct sounds of the animal we were after. I asked Jo if we could proceed to a clearing just up ahead. Hesitantly, she agreed, but the height of the grasses made it difficult to navigate safely. My boots were already on the ground to scout our surroundings, making sure we weren't about to plummet off the edge of a cliff or down a ravine. With determination to encounter an elephant, I marched forward into the unknown. I made it about ten yards from the Land Cruiser, confirmed that the coast was clear to proceed, and then came to the haunting realization of where I was. *I'm on the predator side of the sanctuary*, I thought, *and just because I can't see any lions doesn't mean the lions can't see me!*

I stopped dead in my tracks, listening with bated breath, and slowly turned back toward the vehicle. With my heart racing, I shuffled as quickly as I could back into the Land Cruiser. I relayed my recon to Jo: The road ahead was free of danger, so we continued forward. Slowly, we motored through the grasses, rounded a few crowded bushes, and then arrived at a modest clearing, the perfect place to stop and wait. We sat in silence for no more than a minute when...*Crack!* I heard a branch break, then *sssnap*—another. I scanned the tree tops, and saw them swaying with more force than the current breeze could produce. A gruff *harrumph* sounded out from the bush. This was it...an elephant was coming straight for us!

I quickly turned to the cameras. "This is intense, guys," I whispered. "The bull is just on the other side of these trees."

We couldn't yet tell whether the approaching giant was male or female, nor could we determine if it was the highly sought-after Big Tusker. However, Jo strongly suspected it was a male because, after puberty, males leave their herd and either travel alone—like the Big Tusker—or with another subadult male. Elephant herds are typically comprised of about ten females and their calves, and they're led by a matriarch, an experienced older female. The animal lumbering through the foliage ahead of us definitely wasn't with a herd, but we couldn't quite tell if it was alone based on the movement of the trees.

My heart continued to race as the cameras kept rolling. The animal or animals were getting closer and we had no idea how they would react to our sudden presence. A Land Cruiser full of humans on safari is certainly something they would have seen before, but their behavior is unpredictable. Elephants can be very temperamental and if provoked to charge, they can barrel through the environment at speeds up to fifteen miles per hour, possibly smashing into us with the force of a car crash.

The tension in the air was so thick you could cut it with a knife! Branches kept breaking, and closer treetops were heaving side to side as they made way for whatever was about to emerge from the woods. I saw something bright bobbing through the brush, then finally we made eye contact with an elephant!

"I see the tusks!" I whispered to the camera. Time seemed to slow and we watched with wonder as a subadult male elephant emerged out of the thickets, his long trunk waving as he came to an easy stop. Seeing an elephant in the wild is life changing. Their elegance is unmatched, and their power is undeniable. Words barely escaped my mouth as the lumbering giant approached us.

He wasn't the Big Tusker, but he was still an impressive elephant! He quickly noticed the vehicle full of humans and lifted his massive ears, nearly doubling the width of his head. Like sonar dishes, they homed in on the unnatural object before him, and in that instant, I think it's fair to say that all of our

hearts sank. This was a display of dominance, a message that *I am on high alert and* you *should not be here.* Was he going to charge? Was he going to flip our Land Cruiser with his long, muscular trunk and intimidating ivory tusks? And would he then trample us all under the weight of his powerful legs and feet?! I had never been more frozen with uncertainty than when

Chapter 9 / The Enormous Elephant Encounter!

I was staring down this young bull elephant. He cautiously approached the vehicle and sized us up, stopping just forty feet away. *Whoa buddy*, I thought. *That's close enough!*

Eyeing us from a safe distance, he snaked his trunk around a bushel of foliage and wrenched it into his mouth. His ears relaxed, his eyes drooped, and he lowered his guard, deciding we were nonthreatening and definitely not worth the energy to confront. *Phew*, I thought. That was about as close a call as I think you can have with an elephant, but our encounter wasn't over yet. Just as I was about to breathe a sigh of relief, a second, smaller male elephant appeared from the shadows. Unalarmed and curious, he hid behind the first, peering from behind him and snagging mouthfuls of grass and shrub within reach of his dexterous trunk. Two enormous male African elephants in one encounter?! Mark, Mario, Jo, and I had somehow put ourselves in the right place at exactly the right time!

Elephants are tremendously smart, have remarkable memories, and are totally in tune with their environment, so it was clear these males held no illusions about what we were. Although we were a sizable object as four human beings in a vehicle—something they'd seen before—they were *not* intimidated. Playfully, the larger animal in front of me stepped forward, chewing on his late-morning snack. Probing the air with his trunk, he swayed closer, and was now just twenty feet in front of us. His partner was completely preoccupied and turned his attention to a tasty flowering shrub.

The curious male stepped closer, just ten feet away! Unsure

of his intentions, I found myself standing on the seats. I reached
my arm up and out in front of me, my fingers loosely spread
and my palm flat. His ears flared, but he stopped, looking at
me and my companions curiously. I have never felt so small
in my life. This elephant could have squashed us like jelly, but
instead, he raised his trunk triumphantly—then turned his full
attention to the smaller elephant, now lazily lounging on his
side, and decided to engage *him*! Because the second elephant
was lying on the ground, he must have seemed like a perfect
target. As the larger elephant marched toward him, the smaller
one quickly scrambled to his feet to fend off a full-on attack.

FUMP! The two bulls began butting heads, their tusks
and trunks tangling together as their ears splayed out. It was

hard to tell what was happening—they could have been playing, though I suspected it was territorial dominance—but it was positively riveting. With every lunge forward, every stomp and every push, the ground shook beneath us. Tree branches were snapping right and left, and as these two giants battled each other right before our very eyes, I couldn't believe what a perfect moment I'd found myself in.

Bellowing at a low gravely rumble, the larger male shoved his head to the side, knocking back his challenger. Just when things started to get really dramatic, the spectacle turned toward us! The smaller of the two elephants pulled away, clearly frustrated, and deliberately marched right behind our vehicle. I did say elephants were intelligent, didn't I? Rather than fend off his opponent, the younger bull decided to use our Land Cruiser as a barrier between himself and the other elephant. At this point, everyone was nervous; the last thing we expected was to be part of the action, and knowing how quickly this situation could go from bad to worse, Jo decided she had better step in and make our presence known.

"Hey, go on!" she yelled. The loud holler didn't seem to distract the rumbling beasts at all, but it at least reminded them that a band of admirers was in the vicinity, and squishing them would not be cool. Jo definitely meant business, and though she remained calm, I picked up on the tension rising in her voice. "*HEY!*" she rasped. Mark and Mario were still rolling cameras, and I was on the edge of my seat, ready to join Jo if the beasts didn't back down. It's difficult to describe the anxiety

I felt being trapped in the middle of two warring titans, but I remember a barrage of excited emotions and nervous thoughts as adrenaline coursed through my whole body, causing my hair to stand on end and my stomach to do somersaults. It was one of the most potentially dangerous situations I've experienced in my entire life!

I breathed an elephant-size sigh of relief when the instigator backed down. He snorted, pointed his trunk at his target, and—almost as if in response to Jo—let out a low grumble you could feel in your ribs, as he side-stepped away from us. Smiles broke the tension on our faces as we watched them charge into a grove of acacia trees, blowing muffled trumpeting sounds while they jostled their enormous bodies right back into the brush and out of sight.

"I have never been in a situation like that before," Jo finally said as we drove away. "That was about as close a call as it gets. Hope you caught all that on camera."

Boy, did we! The mission of capturing a wild elephant on camera was our goal, but to see two of them going tusk to tusk in a monster melee, that was unbelievable! The universe had somehow magically placed us in the perfect spot. Maybe it was fate. Or maybe it was just that simple good fortune of being in the right place at the right time. No matter what you believe, it was a dream encounter that we would never be able to replicate.

For me, Mark, and Mario, we felt as if we had the episode in the can, and it was time to call it a day. I mean, come on...we'd just survived an elephant battle royale; how could things possibly get any better?

Thirty minutes later we had made our way from the underbrush and were now driving back on a crumbly gravel road. Bumping along, the Land Cruiser flung sprays of dirt and rocks as we came around a tight corner, lined on either side by tall trees. We were chatting happily, recounting our favorite "intense" moments from the elephant battle and envisioning our final destination: Kariega's main lodge, where a delicious lunch awaited us. All of a sudden...we saw *him*.

"Look right there, right there," Jo said, bringing the Land Cruiser to a jerking halt.

I couldn't believe my own eyes. Standing there right on the side of the road was the one and only Big Tusker!

"Wow!" I exclaimed, totally in awe of his size. The elephant was no more than twenty yards away, and his presence seemed

to weigh more than he did. "If you thought the elephants we saw on the hill were big, they don't even compare to this giant!"

A full grown elephant typically weighs between six thousand and thirteen thousand pounds. Before the expedition began, Jo had told us that the Big Tusker was on the high end of that spectrum, tipping the scales at an estimated six tons, or twelve thousand pounds. The behemoth who stood before us was nearly twice the size of the subadults we had encountered earlier that morning, and we felt positively minuscule looking up at him. With extreme caution, Jo began to inch the truck forward, bringing his full form into plain view. We all gasped. The Big Tusker was a figurative mountain, and as he crossed the road, led forward by the sway of his trunk, we watched his leathery flesh ripple over the tons of muscle that armed his ancient skeleton. His iconic curved tusks were picture-book perfect, over five feet long and capable of humbling even the boldest of competitors. This was the biggest land animal I'd seen in my life, and I simply could not believe it.

"Look at that, you can see his back is covered in mud," I pointed out.

Suddenly, a thought hit me. The tracks and disturbed soil we'd seen earlier this morning must have been from this elephant. He had clearly found a fresh watering hole, as the dirt had been splattered with a new layer of mud, caked into the wrinkles and creases of his skin. The circular prints I stood in had to be his—the animal we'd just missed earlier that morning had been the Big Tusker!

"Look at him," I added. "Just feasting on the tree; he's using his trunk to pull off clumps of leaves and then shoves them into his mouth." His thick, dexterous trunk was as flexible as a snake,

and strong enough to lift over five hundred pounds. Incredibly, there are no bones in this appendage; instead they are composed of over forty thousand muscles!

Elephants are herbivores, and to sustain their impressive size, they eat three hundred to four hundred pounds of grasses, leaves, fruits, bamboo, bark, tree limbs, or roots every single day, selectively clearing entire forests and fields. Jo moved the vehicle closer and we gawked up at the Big Tusker enjoying his early lunch. Then, as any good director should, Mark had a crazy idea!

"Hey, Coyote, it's kind of tough to really put this elephant into scale on camera. We need something in the foreground. How would you feel about getting a little bit closer on foot?"

Then I turned to Jo off camera. "Jo, I gotta give the audience something for scale. What do you think?"

Jo was rightfully cautious, and after what we'd been through with the two subadults, she didn't like the idea of pushing our luck. She looked at me incredulously, looked back at the munching elephant, and then at Mark.

"You cannot get out of the vehicle," she answered firmly. "You just cannot."

I knew she was looking out for my safety, and it *was* a crazy idea, but I was not going to take no for an answer. "I have to get out of the vehicle," I said. "I'll get back in the second you tell me to, but we have to capitalize on this moment. Scale is everything, and without me in the shot, you can't comprehend how big he truly is."

Chapter 9 / The Enormous Elephant Encounter!

Jo paused for a moment, then finally relented. "Okay, here's what we're going to do," she said, turning the car around so that it was parallel to the Big Tusker. "You can get out and take a few steps, but keep yourself low and nonthreatening. If the elephant advances, do not turn your back and do not run. Backpedal quickly and come around the back of the truck so it creates a barrier. If it catches up to you and hits the vehicle, at least it will smash the truck and not your bones."

I nodded my head, then got out just as Jo instructed and crept cautiously toward the feasting beast. When I got close enough that I thought you could sense his scale next to me, I stopped.

"You can see how enormous this elephant is," I said, turning to face him. "I would guess that at the arc of his shoulder right there, he is close to thirteen feet in height. Now, for scale, an NBA basketball hoop is ten feet. I would say even LeBron James would have trouble touching the back of that elephant!" I lingered alongside him as he calmly strolled through the brush, grazing on fresh greens.

My heart was absolutely racing, and I wanted more than anything to get even closer, so I kept myself low to the ground, moving slowly and steadily inch by inch. But the Big Tusker was now on to my bravery and swiftly responded with a show of his might. In the blink of an eye, he lurched forward, tackling the tree in front of him, eliminating the only paltry obstacle between us. The weight of his motion had enough sheer force to crush the tree, and with his ears flared out, he

towered above me as he released a deep reverberating grumble I
could feel in my core. He may as well have been a Tyrannosaurs
Rex, and I may as well have been a mouse. Immediately, I rose
to my feet, sensing he was about to charge if I didn't back down.

"Come back, come back, come back," whispered Jo
insistently. I knew I had to hold my ground and not let the
elephant see how afraid I was, so I didn't run, and I didn't turn
my back. Instead, I put my hand up, and slowly started to step
backward. At this point, I had moved several yards from the

safety of the Land Cruiser, but never lost sight of my refuge.
Calmly and confidently, I retreated across the road and toward
the opposite side of the vehicle, just as Jo had instructed. With
my heart still pounding, I got in the truck and sat back into my
seat. That was without question the furthest I could push that
encounter without risking my life and the lives of those brave
enough to adventure alongside me.

I turned to the camera, delivered an excited wrap-up to our
morning and signed off in classic fashion: "I'm Coyote Peterson.
Be Brave...Stay Wild—we'll see ya on the next adventure!" It
was time to go home.

Our cherished moment in time filming the Big Tusker was
short but sweet—nothing more than fifteen minutes—but it
was truly unforgettable. I love and am incredibly proud of that
episode. It's fun because every time I watch it, my heart skips
a beat when I see that colossal titan rip down the tree and flare
out his ears. In the moment, it was impossible to realize just how
potentially dangerous that brief posturing was, and, boy, am I
thankful he didn't charge.

The African elephant is now considered an endangered
species, and since 1979 over 50 percent of their range has
disappeared. There are only around four hundred fifty thousand
African elephants alive in the world today, and sadly, their
numbers continue to dwindle. Human encroachment, defense of
farming, and poaching—due to man's greedy desire for ivory—
continue to threaten the survival of these beautiful creatures,
and it's up to places like the Kariega Game Reserve to keep

the elephant population wild and strong. I'm so thankful that our preparation and luck had allowed us to witness elephants in the wild, especially the Big Tusker, as his fortitude and majesty epitomizes his species as our planets most impressive land animal. And I hope that by sharing our story and our admiration for these titans you, too, will see the beauty in African elephants and support their ongoing preservation and protection.

Chapter Ten
Phantom of the Wilderness!

Chapter 10 / Phantom of the Wilderness!

B elieve in the impossible and always follow your dreams. When you're young, this may be a hard thing to comprehend, especially when your dreams feel so big and out of reach. I know you all have dreams, and I know that it can be frustrating to think about them all the time, wondering if they'll ever become more than mere fantasies. But you have to keep believing. Dreams *can* come true, but you have to work hard to *make* them come true. Trust me; I'm living proof that it can be done. This chapter is one of those dreams, and it began when I was only eight years old. I dreamed that, with persistence, determination, and patience, I would one day venture into the untouched wilderness of Alaska, and come face-to-snout with one of the planet's most ferocious predators, the wolverine. To me, this elusive creature represented fearlessness, strength, and the majesty of nature.

Many of you are probably familiar with wolverines because of the famous X-Men character played by Hugh Jackman, but when I was a kid, information about the actual animal was nearly impossible to find. In fact, I hadn't even heard of a wolverine till I was in first grade, when I stumbled upon a book in the library that contained an amazing drawing of one ripping apart a frontiersman's cabin. *What is this creature that looks like a bear mixed with a wolf?* I asked myself, totally mesmerized. *It's the coolest animal ever!*

From that moment on, the wolverine was my spirit animal. In the afternoons after school, my mom would drop me off at the library, and I would spend countless hours scouring books to find more information on wolverines. These weren't storybooks or cartoons, either; they were dense field guides with tiny type and huge words I had to sound out with my mom's help. But I studied them carefully, day after day, and I learned that the wolverine is the largest terrestrial mammal of the weasel family, bigger and more ferocious than martens, fishers, and even badgers. They are armed with fixed, razor-sharp claws that extend from their large padded feet, and possess a bite force that is capable of crushing a large mammal's esophagus.

Wolverines are also incredibly intelligent, and they've been known to track a pack of wolves, wait for them to take down a large caribou or elk, then pounce—running in circles, biting the wolves' legs, and eventually driving them away from the carcass. As their Latin name *Gulo*—meaning *glutton*—might suggest, wolverines are voracious eaters. They are opportunistic and omnivorous, which means that they will eat plants, carrion, meat, and even insect larvae when food is scarce. Nomadic and solitary, they range through the arctic and subarctic regions of North America, Europe, and Asia.

Chapter 10 / Phantom of the Wilderness!

While wolverines are rarely seen in the wild, they've been known to break into houses (like the cabin I saw in the book), where they will rummage through pantries and refrigerators looking for a free meal. This curious search is quite destructive, and if trashing the place wasn't enough, their last calling card is to mark the entire area with a pungent musk! Basically, imagine a giant skunk destroying your kitchen. That's what the aftermath would look and smell like. When a wolverine breaks into a cabin to search for a snack, it leaves a wake of destruction in its path. These big balls of fur are calculated chaos, and their spastic energy positively leaped off the page and right into my imagination.

I traced hundreds of pictures of them, and even begged my mom for a toy wolverine. I didn't care if it was plastic, rubber, or soft and plushy, I wanted my very own wolverine more than anything. In the winter of 1989, toy wolverines didn't exactly line the shelves, and no matter where she looked, she couldn't find one. So, determined to fulfill my wish, my mom made me a plush wolverine by hand, and it was better than anything I imagined. Yeah, it's fair to say that my mom is pretty awesome.

I named my new best friend Gulo, after the scientific name for wolverines, *Gulo gulo. Someday, Gulo*, I said to him every night before falling asleep, *we'll meet a real wolverine. Trust me, buddy, it's going to be amazing.*

The only problem, though, is that you have about as much chance of seeing a wolverine in the wild—even for one, fleeting second—as you do Bigfoot. Okay, so maybe they aren't *that* mythological, but still, they are incredibly rare. Wolverines have fantastic senses of smell and can pick up traces of a threat from miles away. Curious and cunning, they may not immediately flee, but will stay completely hidden as they suss out any intruders. A wolverine might see you, but it's very unlikely that *you* will ever see *it*. So when the Brave Wilderness crew and I traveled to Alaska in the summer of 2016, I arrived with a well-formed dream. We knew it was going to be nearly impossible, but our most important goal was to search for and find this phantom of the wilderness.

———

Throughout my life, I have always had a fascination with the mysterious, wild, great northern state of Alaska. I've seen beautiful photos of its pristine forests, towering peaks, and placid lakes, and I watched films where it's often depicted as an unexplored, rugged, and harsh wilderness. But trust me when I say that encountering our forty-ninth state in the flesh totally surpassed my expectations. Alaska is unbelievably huge in all respects. The sky is seemingly endless, and the white-capped mountain ranges dominate the horizon, taller than anything you have ever seen. The densely forested roads seem to stretch into infinity, and the numerous flowing rivers work like intricate ropes that tie it all together. Although the landscape is gorgeous, it's also packed with danger. Aside from its many environmental obstacles, the most obvious dangers come in the form of its predatory mammals, including wolves, black bears, and of course, grizzly bears. So as the Brave Wilderness team and I set out into the wild with the hopes of spotting a wolverine, we were constantly aware that a grizzly may be lurking around any turn. And if you remember what happened in "Chapter 7: BEAR SCARE!" of *Brave Adventures: Wild Animals in a Wild World*, then you know that we found ourselves in that very situation.

For several days the team and I put in our best efforts at finding a wolverine in the wild, but I'm sure you're not surprised to hear that we came up short on our quest. Not just that, but I never even saw a track, a snagged cluster of hair in the brambles, or even a single wolverine dropping. In the end, the phantom of the wilderness eluded us in all respects. To be completely fair, we kind of knew this would be the case, so before embarking upon this grand adventure to Alaska, we devised a backup plan—working with a wolverine in captivity. And there was only one man in the world who could provide us with that experience: Steve Kroschel. Steve is a fascinating, brilliant, and unfathomably talented man who runs the Kroschel Wildlife Sanctuary in Haines, Alaska.

Steve is a naturalist through and through. He grew up on a farm in northern Minnesota, where he and his family rescued, rehabilitated, and raised orphaned wildlife, a passion and expertise that he eventually took with him to Alaska. There, he founded his sanctuary, which today is home to several of Alaska's native species including lynx, wolves, foxes, moose, pine martens, porcupines, and believe it or not, a wolverine named Banff, who he rescued after his mother was killed by fur trappers. Steve is also a renowned filmmaker, famous for his death-defying footage of avalanches, so I knew right away that if there was anyone brave enough to befriend and tussle with a wolverine, it was Steve.

"When you come visit, park down at the bottom of the hill, and I'll come meet you," Steve said on the phone when I called.

That was easy! I thought. *Even if I don't find a wolverine in the wild, Steve will introduce me to one!* Well, not quite. Steve is justifiably cautious about introducing his ferocious friend to strangers, and if I wanted the kind of encounter I dreamed about, I would have to prove that I was worthy. Once again, trust would be the key to fulfilling my dreams. Before he would let me meet Banff, I'd have to work hard to get Steve to believe in me—and then work *even harder* to gain the confidence of the wolverine!

———

Our plan was to shoot the wolverine episode all in one day, so Mark, Mario, and I rose early and drove to meet

Steve, parking on the road outside his sanctuary. We climbed the long gravel hill up to the gate, shrouded with huge hemlocks and oversize ferns. When we arrived, the door was closed, and hanging across it we noticed to a rather cryptic-looking sign.

"That's a little creepy, *Extreme danger! Closed! No entry!*" said Mark, as he peered over the fence in search of our host. "And there's a padlock on it. Are you sure he's expecting us?"

"Yeah, we told Steve we were coming this morning," I answered. "I think we should just go in."

Chapter 10 / Phantom of the Wilderness!

It turned out the padlock was open, so we pushed through the gates, entered the sanctuary, and continued our hike up the hill…up, up, and past a few weathered cabins that were overgrown with brush. As I clutched Gulo in my arms, my heart was about to explode with excitement. First, though, I had to meet Steve, and I wasn't sure what to expect. I'd heard he was a bit of a wild man, but no more than any person living with a bunch of animals in a remote corner of Alaska. Right? When Steve spotted us, he shuffled down the hill, extending his hand out to meet me, and my jaw dropped. *Who is this man?* I thought.

Steve had bright, wide eyes and wore several eagle feathers in the top of his knit cap. He was beaming with positivity and passion, and moved with absolutely electric energy. He walked fast and talked even faster, and when he zipped from animal enclosure to animal enclosure—barefoot, of course, because he said it makes him feel closer to the Earth—I started to wonder if he might be a bit of a wolverine himself. With him, he carried a tattered and torn forest-green, long-sleeved shirt. It had muddy paw prints down the back and claw marks torn along the arms. What was I in for?

The sanctuary was unlike anywhere I had ever been. It had several log cabins—all decorated with antlers from caribou, moose, and elk—a handful of sheds, and numerous pathways leading to different animal enclosures. On most of the cabins, there were handwritten phrases about positivity and presence, like *Right now is a gift, that's why it's called the present.* Everything around us was fully immersed in the overgrowth of the forest, and the enclosures seemed to blend in with the landscape that surrounded us. After our inital greeting, Steve and I walked over to a log, sat down, and plotted out our plan for the day.

"Meeting a wolverine has been a dream of mine since I was eight years old," I told him as we sat side by side, trying to sort out what I should expect that day. "You can help me realize that today, if you're willing to train me and let me get close."

Steve's eyes grew huge, and he lowered his gaze, clenched his jaw, and shook his head back and forth. "How much time do we have?" he asked.

"Well," I answered, "I need to get this episode today, so it's eight o'clock now—"

Steve interrupted. "T-today? Today?"

"Today," I said firmly. "Eight hours. Can you turn me into someone who's ready to be in an enclosure with a wolverine in eight hours?" I stared at Steve intently. *Please say yes!*

Steve didn't say anything, but just shook his head, laughing at the idea. My heart sank. I'd come all the way to Alaska to meet a wolverine, and I wasn't taking no for an answer. This was my dream, and even though we just met, I knew I had to get Steve to trust me. He looked up at me in disbelief, and with as much seriousness and intensity as I could, I made my appeal: "If you're willing to train me, I'm willing to do whatever it takes."

"Train you?" he asked.

"Train me," I insisted. "To the point where you feel I'm ready to be in the presence of a wolverine."

Steve looked down, muttered a few words, and chuckled again. But I could see a sly smile cross his face, and right away, I knew I'd convinced him. I was going to get to meet a wolverine!

Steve's plan was to build me up mind, body, and soul to the point that I'd be emotionally and physically ready to meet Banff. After passing some rigorous tests—and I had no clue what they'd be—I'd get the chance to walk Banff on a lead and harness, and if he accepted me, enter into his enclosure. Of course, Steve would also be present for safety's sake, but he'd take the harness off Banff, allowing the animal to roam free without any restraints or barriers. This would mean that I would be inside an enclosure with an unharnessed snarly wolverine. It sounded perfect!

I was pretty anxious both to prove myself to Steve and to learn from him, so I stood up and took off my shoes. If I was going to learn from the wolverine master, I needed to dress like the wolverine master—like Steve. I wanted to be barefoot for my day of training. Following close behind, I scampered after him, trying to keep up as he hustled up a hill, deeper into the woods of the sanctuary. We soon rounded a bend in the road where we passed a glass case containing several skulls—one of which I knew was that of a wolverine.

Coyote Pack, let me just tell you that I felt like some invisible force was compelling me to stop and look. I'd seen wolverine skulls behind glass in museums, but I'd never in my life held one in my hands. I called out to Steve, asking him if he would let me take it out. I wanted to examine its form and show the camera the big brain cavity and those powerful jaws. I certainly was not intending to be bitten by Banff, but I was curious as to how sharp a wolverine's teeth actually were.

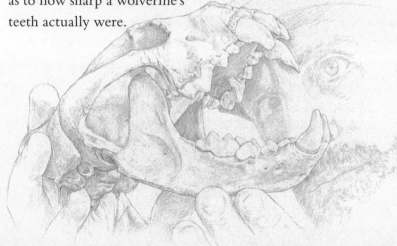

Chapter 10 / Phantom of the Wilderness!

So I asked Steve to hold the skull, open the jaws, and then clamp it down on my outstretched hand. Steve looked at me as if I were crazy, but he did as I requested and ratcheted down with a fair amount of force. *Ouch!* Wolverines' teeth are incredibly sharp and if this had been Banff, the jaws would be strong enough to crush bone. Steve released pressure on the skull to give me back my hand, and when I looked down I wasn't surprised in the slightest to see that the teeth had left deep bite mark impressions on my skin.

Now it was time to knuckle down and prove my mettle. No guts, no glory! Luckily, Steve's first test for me seemed deceptively easy. One of the sanctuaries rescued and rehabilitated animals was a pine marten: a long, slender mammal who's related to, though is significantly smaller than, a wolverine. This feisty little mustelid was scurrying through some pipes that extended out of a small dilapidated timber shed. It was a unique enclosure and was the perfect design for an animal who likes to climb trees and stay hidden in hollows. Steve wanted to see if I could feed it without getting my fingers bitten off. So he walked to his house, returned with a jar of jelly, and asked me to place some on the end of a stick. I then held the stick up to the entrance of the enclosure and waited for Steve to slide open the door. I waited…and waited…and suddenly heard the scampering of feet and a high-pitched growling behind the door.

"No, I can't do it!" yelled Steve, a look of terror on his face.

His outburst startled me, and my heart started pounding. I

wasn't sure if the sound of fear in his voice was meant to rattle me—seeing how I would do under pressure—or if he was legitimately worried I'd lose a finger to the marten's razor-sharp teeth. Not wanting to show any insecurity, I kept my composure and yelled right back, "I can do it! I can do it!"

"It'll bite you in the face!" Steve screamed.

I tried to sound confident. "I can do it! Count me down!"

"One, two…*ayyy yay yay*!" Before he even got to three, Steve opened the door, and a terrifying, weasel-like creature popped its triangular head out of the enclosure, clenched the stick with its dagger-like chompers, and retreated back into its

hidey-hole as quickly as it had emerged. Oh my gosh, it was like a velociraptor from *Jurassic Park* had just snapped his jaws at me! Luckily, though, I still had my fingers, which means I'd passed the first test!

But it wasn't over yet—not even close. In order to get Banff to trust me, Steve decided I had to give him a peace offering. Wolverines are notorious scavengers, following wolves and even bears for days to pick up whatever scraps they leave behind. During the winter months when food is scarce, they'll even store their scavenged carrion deep in the snow to keep it fresh, returning days later to resume their meal. Steve assured me that Banff liked meat no matter what condition it was in, so he told me to pick out a big section from one of the drying moose hides that were hanging on the side of an old weathered cabin, and cut a piece out that I *felt* Banff would like. This doesn't *sound* so bad, but, boy, did it smell awful. Much of the moose hide was still wet and rotting, and the stench was so strong that you could almost taste it in the air.

"You're going to put feeling into it, even when you're cutting it," Steve said. "You're going to think about the wolverine's feelings. You're getting into its frequency. You're dialing in!"

Forget frequency. As I was cutting it, all I could think about was how rancid the hide was, and I must have been too hasty because the first piece I cut was too small.

"Bigger!" Steve yelled. "That looks like you're insulting him!"

Chapter 10 / Phantom of the Wilderness!

Well, I certainly don't want to do that, I thought. Gripping the hide by the handful, I sawed into it with gusto, cutting off a huge piece of the wet stuff for Banff. I felt it slip in my fingers as I pulled the piece free, and I started to retch. I held my breath and hurried away from the shed, carrying the decomposing mammal skin into a large enclosure that looked like a mix between a gladiator ring and a wilderness movie set.

Upon entering the wolverine's arena, my nose was drawn away from the smell of the moose to the distinct, musky scent of Alaska's largest mustelid. It was like a combination of wet skunk and dog fart mingling in a dank, musty basement. Think that sounds bad? Well...*it smells even worse!*

"The sense of smell on a wolverine is very, very keen," said Steve as he instructed me to rub the rotting hide all over the inside of the wolverine's enclosure. "One molecule per five million. Yours is like one molecule per one hundred twenty-five thousand."

I'm sure glad my sense of smell isn't better! I thought as I dragged the nasty hide across the ground, the logs, and the fence. Steve said that this grotesque ritual gave the wolverine an exciting scent to chase, and given that this is one of his most powerful attributes, marking its environment with this pungent odor would quickly get his attention.

I thought the worst had to be over, but it wasn't. Before I'd even had a chance to wash my hands, Steve ordered me to retrieve a forty-pound slab of cow ribs from a cooler in his house, then march it up a gravel hill, barefoot, for about a mile. As my feet ground into rocks and my muscles strained, I felt like Rocky Balboa (cue the music)...if Rocky had smelled like rotting moose flesh.

"Bury it just enough," Steve told me when I got into the wolverine's enclosure. I gathered a pile of loose grass, wedged the ribs between a few boulders, and blanketed it with green, so that Banff would have to use his instincts to find it. "You don't want to insult the wolverine's intelligence. Do not make it feel stupid, because it will know. That's why you can't just give him a treat like a dog. He will call you out on that and *not* be happy."

Hours passed in the blink of an eye, and before I knew it the summer sun was directly overhead. I could feel sweat trickling down my back from hauling the cow ribs up the hill, and my shirt was stuck to my shoulders. According to Steve, however, I still wasn't ready to meet the wolverine. So he had me run *more*—sprinting up and down another hill until my lungs burned and I could barely breathe. When I was done with that, I took a quick rest, then balanced on a stump with one leg for several minutes until my muscles ached, just like the

Karate Kid. By the time that was over, I was so tired I thought I might collapse, and when Steve told me to go into the wolverine's arena and take a nap on a log, I almost hugged him.

"If you fall asleep to the sound of the raven, it will lead you to a dream that will tell you of your destiny," he said.

I entered the enclosure, lay down on a long flat log, put my hat over my face, and closed my eyes. My mind started to wander, and within seconds, I started to drift off. I didn't sense my destiny as much as realize that there was a method to Steve's madness. He wasn't just trying to condition me so that I could survive a physical encounter with a wolverine. He was also thinking, *How far can I push this guy and his little wolverine plushy before he cracks?* He knew, just like I did, that being in the presence of the wolverine had an inherently spiritual dimension, and I had to want it from deep within my soul.

Without question, I did, but even people who've been obsessed with wolverines for most of their lives reach breaking points, and mine came just after I woke up. Steve owned a huge metal bear trap that was once used by fur trappers to catch Kodiak bears. It was so strong, it was capable of snapping a thick piece of hardwood in half, and Steve set it up, put his arm in it, and pulled the trigger. *Snap!* Its massive metal jaws sprang shut, but Steve whipped his arm out just in the nick of time.

"This test is about precision, timing, focus, and speed," he said. "A wolverine can strike as fast as a bear trap, and you need to be faster. So put your arm in there."

I shook my head. My arm wasn't going anywhere near that bear trap! "I totally respect that, Steve," I said, "but I'm not going to do it." I knew Steve wasn't testing my speed; he was testing my knowledge. Early frontiersmen had documented countless instances of wolverines robbing their fur traps without getting caught. If this animal was smart enough to avoid the metal jaws, so was I.

I had one more skill set to learn, and that was to master the vocalizations it would take to interact with the wolverine. As we stood in the driveway, just out of earshot of the wolverine, Steve taught me a series of guttural, high-pitched, animalistic noises that sounded like a screaming goat. I felt a little absurd, but apparently this is what would save me from a full-blown attack if the wolverine became aggressive. Alternatively, he taught me some softer, baby-like sounds that would offer Banff positive reinforcement, telling him that I was a friend and not a threat.

I listened carefully and observed his body language, and no matter how strange it might have looked, there was a reason for every gesture and every sound. I replicated them with as much commitment and intent as I could.

"The next step is that you can see the wolverine," Steve said, sitting me down. "I'm going to have it on a lead. I'll take it out, and we'll see what happens next." And with that, my training was complete.

I did it! I thought, my mind buzzing with anticipation. I put every ounce of effort into gaining Steve's confidence, and now, I was finally ready to meet the phantom of the wilderness!

Stay calm, Coyote, I told myself, *because if this animal senses fear, he will gain the upper hand, knowing he can overpower you.* Wolverines are inherently mischievous, and out in the harsh forests of their natural environment, their ability to perceive a moment's hesitation is the key to their survival. When confronting a bear or wolf over meat, they use their quick wit and agility to out maneuver and outsmart the larger predator, leaving the prize up for grabs.

I took a deep, restorative breath, and Steve emerged from the enclosure with the wolverine. I was awestruck. I don't know if it was Steve's rigorous training or my deep, long-standing desire for this moment, but I felt an instant connection with Banff the moment he sauntered down the path with Steve. This magnificent animal was fifty pounds of pure muscle—the size of a golden retriever—with dark, dense, oily fur so thick that it repels water and snow. I studied how his lustrous brown fur lightened to tan, then darkened to black near his face and his legs, and I marveled at his snowshoe-like paws, which almost double in size when his feet hit the ground. I noticed Banff's crampon-like claws and how they gripped on wood like Velcro as he prowled up a dense gray log. I looked at Steve, awaiting a signal that it was okay to approach. He gave me a confident nod and I focused my gaze toward Banff. I was entranced by this incredible mustelid and it was time to come face-to-snout with the beast I'd spent the last twenty-five years dreaming of.

I calmly walked to the high end of the log as Banff climbed up towards me, sinking his claws into the wood at the top. I was now just three feet away from him, and without hesitation the wolverine and I leaned in, less than an arm's length away from each other. His broad, wet nose approached mine, and I held my breath as we got closer, then closer, then, for one brief moment, we nearly touched noses. Steve pulled Banff back just a bit, and

the animal opened his mouth, a grin of shining white pointed teeth flashing across his face. As his impressive canines glistened in the sun, he extended his paw forward and took a playful swipe in my direction. To Steve, this was a good sign, showing that Banff was comfortable enough to let me interact with him on my own.

As Banff silently bounded from the log, Steve handed me the tether. I gripped the nylon lead tightly in my sweaty palms and took my first steps with a wolverine. It seemed as if I were fully connected to him, not just by the rope, but by some inexplicable force of nature. He regarded me with familiarity, as if I were a part of his world, and without applying any pressure or direction, I let Banff take the lead and follow his curiosity to a huge piece of timber where I had previously rested my plush animal, Gulo. Banff examined my scraggly little stuffed animal with his snout, sniffing and prodding until he knocked it off the log. He lowered his head, opened his mouth, and affectionately licked my prized childhood possession. *This is the first and only stuffed wolverine to ever make contact with a real wolverine*, I thought. *Gulo is truly a legend!* Gulo might be only a toy, but it was as intimately a part of my hero's journey as Steve was.

It's hard to remember what I was thinking in the moment, because I was in a dream state the entire time. I never felt fear or unease as I walked with the wolverine, but instead felt fully grounded and present as I appreciated that once-in-a-lifetime experience. Perhaps I really *had* made a soul connection with Banff, as Steve had taught me, because without question, he was just as calm as I was. Our bond was genuine, and I believe we shared a mutual trust and respect as we navigated the path around the sanctuary.

"Now we gotta go back," Steve said after about five minutes of me walking Banff. I could barely keep up with my thoughts, as I replayed those first minutes in my head on fast forward. When Steve approached me, I handed him the tether, ready for what came next. He stepped into the enclosure, pulled along by the expectant wolverine. Banff must have smelled the pungent moose hide and was occupied with the scent trail I left for him earlier that day. I stepped in the arena. Mark—who'd been filming the whole time—followed after me, and as instructed, we took our places. I crouched down next to the dry hide, which Steve called my "gift," and placed my GoPro on the ground next to it. Mark was in position, I gave a thumbs-up, and Steve unclasped the harness holding back the beast. He hurried over and walked behind me, closely followed by Banff, his nose tracing the smell of his snack as he slinked closer. I grasped the hide in my hands and offered it to him, my heart jumping out of my chest when he eagerly accepted it. He tugged at it with incredible strength, almost pulling me forward off my feet!

"Do I let it go?" I asked Steve, totally in disbelief at what was happening to me.

"No, just let him pull on it."

I held on, and after a brief game of tug-of-war, Steve told me to let go. Banff pulled away his prize; the wolverine had won the war. Suddenly, something else caught the animal's attention,

and he probed around in the grass where I'd hidden the cow ribs. With Steve's permission, I then moved about two feet away from Banff and watched him very deliberately uncover the hidden treat.

"What I want you to do now," Steve said quietly, his voice growing more insistent as he kept talking, "I want you to grab that piece of meat and drag it over here and throw it up on this rock. See if he takes it back. If you do that, you're developing a relationship with him without insulting him...hurry, hurry, hurry!"

I pinched the ribs at one end and dragged the meat several
yards through the grass before heaving it up on to a boulder
in the center of the enclosure. Banff followed—holding his
face close to the ground, almost as if guided entirely by his
nose—and trotted over to me, claiming the rack of ribs with
his claws. He sniffed at it, breathed on it, and hooked it with
his canines, finally finding a point of purchase to pull it down
and drag it back where he wanted it. Remember, Banff is about
fifty pounds, and this cut of meat was about forty! It was easy
to forget that as I watched him yank the gift away over a log,
where he proceeded to nibble on it happily. At this point, I
wasn't thinking anymore; I just let my body move and interact

naturally within his space, exactly as Steve had taught me.

"He's letting you into his private world now," Steve said. "And that is incredible. I just can't believe what I just saw." The relationship between Steve and Banff had been built over several years of experience and care, and just because I had walked with the wolverine on a harness did not mean I had come close to realizing the significance of their trust. To hear Steve recognize this moment with such esteem was incredibly reassuring, because I knew just how in tune he is with his animals.

At one point, Steve gave me his trusty green shirt—the article of clothing he always wore around Banff—to further protect my interactions with the mustelid. Wolverines have semi-retractable claws, meaning that, for the most part, their claws are always exposed. One swipe of a paw would result in rough-cut gashes...and probably stitches. Steve claimed that the sturdy fabric of this shirt had saved him countless times when raising Banff from a kit. If I ever felt aggression from him, the shirt would ensure that I could make a hasty escape before being grappled onto and overpowered. I gratefully put it on.

While Banff was distracted, I snuck over and grabbed the ribs again, dragging them back to my initial position in the arena. He immediately caught on, and defiantly yanked his food back, literally bringing me to my knees! I didn't react, but let him pull on it again, this time bringing me all the way down to my elbows. Then he lurched backward, actually pulling my whole body forward as I clung to the cow meat clenched in his teeth. I sat in a stupor watching Banff razor through the cut of meat, and then, suddenly, he approached me. Surprised, I rocked back on my feet, ready to leap up the moment he showed aggression, but when he got within two paces of my knees he stopped. He raised his large black nose, and as I extended out my arm, we made nose-to-hand contact. *I touched a wolverine*, I thought. *I actually did it!* A buzz of pure joy ran up my arm and down my spine, my mind unable to think straight. Banff shook his whole body, leapt up, and—*fwoosh*—swiped his huge paw through the air in front of me, his mouth agape, revealing all of his sharp bone-crushing teeth. He darted back and forth and then—*bam!*—swatted the camera.

That's when Steve intervened.

"All right, we're done!" he yelled as he shooed Banff away.
I didn't want this magical moment to end, but Steve knew this
creature better than anyone, and he was right. Banff was spastic,
darting this way and that and snapping at the camera. The last
thing we wanted to happen was for Banff to turn me into a
chew toy, but I wanted to push the envelope further. I think I
let my obsession with the wolverine get the best of me because
I tried to persuade Steve to let me stay in the enclosure longer,
but he was having none of it. "Nope, open that door," Steve
said, ushering us out—and then, *boom*. He shut the entrance to
Banff's encosure, and the encounter was over. My time with the
phantom of the wilderness had come to an end.

There are times in your life when the completion
of something feels like a door has been slammed shut,
extinguishing all the light in the room. Unfortunately for me,
this was one of those moments, but safety always comes first.
The well-being of myself, the crew, and, most important, the
animal, is the priority. When I exited the enclosure, my energy
and excitement were at an all-time high. I had just become the
first animal show host in history to have a full-on interaction
with an unharnessed wolverine! What was even more impressive
in my own mind was the fact that I had realized my dream
of working with a wolverine. I was happy. Truly, completely
happy. And when Steve finally emerged from the enclosure, I
got to thank him for all that he'd allowed me to do. I'd realized
my childhood dream by making a connection with Banff. But

what was just as important was that in Steve, I'd found a friend.

As children we are told to follow our dreams. To work hard and never give up. My long journey north into the wilds of Alaska was always one of my dreams, and there were many people who helped to make it a reality. I will always be thankful to Steve for the trust he bestowed upon me and I will forever cherish my moments spent working alongside Banff. He was incredible, just as I had envisioned in my dreams and more.

The realization of dreams is a powerful thing and, in some cases, it may take your entire life to achieve just one. The wolverine was one of my dreams; it is a phantom of the wilderness and to this day remains my true spirit animal. Looking back on it all, I now have a new dream. I dream of one day returning to Alaska to visit my friend and to reconnect with the animal who drew me so far from home. And I hope that when I do, the North will welcome me back with a smile and sharp pair of claws!

Coyote Peterson's Tips for Making Your Dreams Come True

Seek inspiration from the
places you know best.

Expect the unexpected.

Face your fears and take risks.

Always listen to your mentors.

Stop and smell the lions.

Be patient.

Do your homework.

Push your limits.

A little luck goes a long way.

Have faith and never stop believing.

Conclusion

S ince childhood I have been following a series of seemingly impossible dreams, yet as the years go by, I am able to look back and realize that my relentless pursuit has brought many of them to fruition. Looking forward, there are many more dreams still to come and every day I strive to make them a reality. So where does this drive come from? That's a great question, and while it has several long-winded answers, the simplest one is *you*.

If you are reading this book, it means that you are a member of the Coyote Pack. Your enthusiasm for the great outdoors, your interest in reading, and your love of the world of animals is what powers the drive of my current and future dreams. By watching our videos and reading these books, you've helped us paddle down the rivers of Costa Rica; you've led us across the coastal cliffs and into the tide pools of South Africa; and you have even navigated us into the vast, dry terrain that makes up Australia's iconic Outback. You may not have physically been on the expedition, but in our minds and hearts, you were with us every step of the way. I hope that this book has been a wonderful journey, and that along the winding path, you gained some well-earned knowledge. I hope that your imagination was able to run wild like an unharnessed wolverine.

I've always felt that you should trust in your dreams. You can and you will make them come true, I promise. Just never stop believing!

Be Brave...Stay Wild—we'll see you on the next adventure!

Be Brave.
Stay Wild.
Read Fearlessly.